Spiritual ABUSE
RECOVERY WORKBOOK

by DAVID HENKE

An educational and interactive resource to assist you on your path to freedom, healing, and peace.

Watchman Fellowship

Spiritual Abuse Recovery Workbook
Copyright © 2021 by David Henke
Revised and published 2021

Scripture taken from the NEW AMERICAN STANDARD BIBLE, © 1960, 1962, 1963, 1968, 1971, 1973, 1975, 1977, 1995, 2020 by The Lockman Foundation. ... Used by permission.

All rights reserved. No part of this publication may be reproduced, stored in a retrieval system, or transmitted in any form or by any means—electronic, mechanical, photocopy, scanning, recording, or any other—except for brief quotations in printed reviews, without the prior permission of the author.

Published by Watchman Fellowship, Inc.
www.watchman-ga.org

Paperback ISBN: 978-1-7375227-0-6
eBook ISBN: 978-1-7375227-1-3

Dedication

to the "Wounded Sheep" who just wanted to serve God and please Him.

Table of Contents

Foreword

When I was a child, my family became involved with a spiritually abusive group. Subsequently, I spent nearly three decades of my life immersed in that belief system. Since I did not have any point of reference, at first, I thought the behavior I encountered was normal. Nevertheless, it was not a healthy emotional environment. Once I reached adulthood, the spiritual abuse I endured caused me to experience periodic bouts of deep depression and anxiety.

Even so, I held on to the group's theology, believing it to be true. I felt the beliefs were sound, even though some of the behavior among the leadership seemed harsh. I thought that the behavior was a result of imperfection, and God would eventually straighten it out; because after all, it was His group. He would take care of it. What I did not realize, was the behavior I observed was not a remote exception to the groups thinking, but rather supported by it.

Some years ago, someone introduced me to David Henke and his wife, Carole. We spent a very long day together. On that day, I was launched on a journey to true freedom in Christ and a personal relationship with Jesus. The oppression I had been under for nearly 30 years, gave way to joy and a healing of my spirit.

I would like to invite you to "spend a day" with David Henke, as I did years ago. You can do that by reading this workbook. Within the pages of this book, you will have access to his years of research and life experience in assisting people to find freedom and healing, as well as a relationship with God.

It is my privilege to recommend this "Spiritual Abuse Recovery Workbook." Throughout the book, you will come to understand the nature of spiritual abuse, the abusers, and the roles that they play. In the process, I believe you will be able to identify harmful behavior and issues. With your newfound education, I believe that you can find the strength to break free from an unhealthy system and embark on a path to recovery.

You will notice that no groups, unhealthy churches, or cults are mentioned by name within the pages of this workbook. I think you will find this decision by the author to be a wise one. Once you learn how to identify a spiritually abusive group, you can easily apply the principles to groups in the past, the present, and those groups that have yet to be invented. After all, it would be impossible to list them all. Nevertheless, I believe that the education within these pages will protect you from spiritually abusive groups that you may encounter in your life. Armed with this knowledge, you can immediately identify what you are dealing with, and steer clear of involvement with them.

This workbook is an extraordinary resource. It is my prayer that it will be a blessing to you for a lifetime.

—Deborah Dykstra

Preface

"And he gave some as apostles, and some as prophets, and some as evangelists, and some as pastors and teachers, for the equipping of the saints for the work of service, to the building up of the body of Christ.... As a result, we are no longer to be children, tossed here and there by waves, and carried about by every wind of doctrine, by the trickery of men, by craftiness in deceitful scheming."

Ephesians 4:11,12,14

For two millennia God has called humble men with a servant's heart to lead His Church as apostles, prophets, evangelists, and pastors/teachers. These men do not hold their positions to be served, but to serve, for the benefit of the Body of Christ. It is the author's conviction that the vast majority of our spiritual leaders in Bible-believing churches are of this high quality.

The subject of this workbook concerns what the Apostle Paul called the "sleight of men, and cunning craftiness." Not all who hold positions of spiritual leadership were called by God to that service; there will inevitably be some who called themselves. And there will be others who were called of God but were enticed away from following the humble example of Jesus. These men can be crafty and deceitful. Such leaders often wish to be served, not following our Lord's example.

For those who have lost confidence in the Church or its leaders because of a terrible experience, I want to emphasize that you can recover. You can find a healthy church. You can, when you have recovered, place your trust once again in a godly Christian pastor. It is the purpose of this workbook to assist you toward that end.

Introduction

Since 1975, I have been intensely involved in researching, counseling, and writing about religious groups that exert a high level of control over the personal lives of adherents. I am the founder of Watchman Fellowship, one of the leading ministries focused on this issue.

Through the years I have become very familiar with the pain and suffering individuals experienced at the hands of false spiritual leaders. The methods these leaders use to exert control over their followers leads to a loss of freedom of conscience and personal liberty.

Most of the groups I have dealt with are cults that you would recognize if I named them. I will not for one simple reason. My goal is to deal with the dynamics of control in a religious setting. To name any group is to put the focus on that group and therefore take away the focus from the control that is so spiritually and emotionally damaging.

I want you to make the connection between the symptoms and methods I describe and the group of which you were a member. If there are points of connection, you may need the information in this workbook to free yourself from its clutches and begin a process of healing.

What I will describe is not limited to groups that are doctrinally outside the bounds of the Christian faith. **This is a problem that arises from human weakness and need that frequently gets mixed up with religious practices and leads to problems that can affect doctrine or practice.** Human weaknesses will be found in every religion. Someone with a need might use religion to meet that need; if they use it legitimately, then all is well. However, if they misuse religion others are often at risk. Such misuse of religion is called *spiritual abuse*. Usually someone in a position of power or influence is tempted to abuse his authority. The temptation to take shortcuts at the expense of ethics and the needs of followers is very real. I have found that the powerless and weak are seldom the perpetrators, because abuse is an exercise of power.

A prominent place is given in scripture to warnings about false teachers who bring in false doctrines that will ensnare believers and place them in bondage. Every book in the New Testament, except one, Philemon, contains such warnings. In Jesus' own ministry a prominent place is given to His conflict with the spiritual abusers of His day, the Pharisees and religious rulers. In this workbook we will look at the example of the Pharisees and their modern counterparts.

Over the years I have met with groups of what I call "dissidents" who have invited me to help them understand what happened to them in a religious setting. In those meetings I discuss the same things I present in this workbook. In group meetings I ask everyone present to agree not to share what is said with anyone not present. Confidentiality is crucial when discussing personal experiences.

I first describe the characteristics of legalism. From there I go to the marks of spiritually abusive systems. Last, I describe the eight criteria of mind control. At each of these areas, dissidents are given whatever time they need to discuss how a characteristic may have been displayed in their group. They begin slowly, cautious about what they can say, and who will hear them. But as the meeting continues the comments begin to flow. When the meetings are over people express relief that they are not alone in their experience and understanding that they were caught up in a system that stifled their God-given freedom to think and act for themselves.

Some dissidents even identify with the mind control model, the extreme far end of the spectrum of control. As you read the descriptions of mind control you may say, "That is what happened to me." Perhaps. But mind control is a much stronger version of the spiritual abuse characteristics you will read about later. It can literally cause people to *drink the Kool-Aid*. It sounds similar to spiritual abuse because it is operating on the same principles but to a more extreme degree.

I will provide insights into why some people get snared in spiritual bondage, and why others are susceptible to control and abuse. I will describe some of the doctrines and cliché sayings that are used to compel submission. Another fascinating topic will be the five roles that are typically played in high control religious systems. It is important for the individual who struggles with the issues of guilt, shame, and doctrine to know that a comprehensive system was in place to control and manipulate them into submission. Those who bring this kind of abuse on their followers may not even recognize what they are doing. When one falsehood is taught, another falsehood is required to support it, and then another to support that, re-enforcing the injurious system.

I will also describe what you must do to become whole again. If you are in the depths of despair, you may wonder if your life will ever be peaceful again. It can and will if you make healthy choices and avoid those things that bring harm.

My purpose is to describe the Truth and rely on the assurance of scripture that "the truth will set you free." The truth will provide you with the insights you need to discern whether you are experiencing legalism or spiritual abuse. It will give you direction so that you can gain freedom from the abusive control of others and find healing. The truth will also show you how you can turn your bad experience into a blessing to yourself and to others.

Some of the problems I will describe arise from personal needs that are met by illegitimate means that the perpetrator does not recognize as being illegitimate. He may respond to being taught. There may also be psychological problems that give rise to his abuse, or to a follower's submission to false spiritual leadership. In such a case a licensed counselor should be consulted.

It is my earnest hope that this workbook can help you process your experience, just as others have when they learned more, and were able to think through the implications of this information.

"The LORD is my light and my salvation; whom shall I fear?
The LORD is the defense of my life; whom shall I dread?"
Psalm 27:1

—David Henke

1

Spiritual Abuse

"Men do not differ much about what things they call evils;
they differ enormously about what evils they will call excusable."
G.K. Chesterton

SPIRITUAL ABUSE DEFINED

A simple definition of spiritual abuse is *the injury of a person's spiritual health by the misuse of their trust to gain or maintain control over them and to use them or their resources for the benefit of the leader or group.*

Spiritual abuse occurs when someone holding a position of spiritual influence, leadership, or authority uses that position to benefit themselves at the expense of the individuals whom they are ostensibly there to help. Spiritual abuse crosses personal boundaries without permission and does some of the greatest damage that can be done.

Jeff VanVonderen, author of *The Subtle Power of Spiritual Abuse*, said that the symptoms of someone who has experienced spiritual abuse are the same as those exhibited by victims of incest. The common denominator between the two is that the parent and the spiritual leader are both the most intimate caregivers, and the boundaries they cross are the most intimate. Therefore, the damage is far greater. It strikes at the very soul of the person. The victims then withdraw from the source of their injury, whether it is the opposite sex or the spiritual leader. They fear letting themselves be "touched" again. In the case of spiritual abuse, the church represents trauma and not refuge. Therefore, so many abuse victims leave church and don't come back for years—or sometimes, never.

Those who attempt to advise victims of spiritual abuse MUST know that the victim is telling the truth. This is not something "whiners" can imitate. One of the reasons spiritual abuse reaches deep into a person's soul is that church is a refuge from the world. We expect to be able to let our guard down among our best friends, fellow Christians. We expect our spiritual leaders to lead us wisely. When the shepherds beat God's sheep, as in Ezekiel 34, it is so completely unexpected that we don't know how to process it.

When advising spiritual abuse victims, never say "Get over it" or, "Just put it behind you." This is not a simple offense like gossip. It is like losing a limb. Victims can adjust, compensate, or make do, but they cannot just get over it. It would be like telling a paraplegic to just get over it! It is like a huge part of the person's soul has been ripped out, leaving a vacuum. He will never be the same again. Gone is the innocent trust of spiritual leaders. He doubts first and trusts later, MAYBE.

There is some deficiency in the psychological profile of the abusive leader that motivates him to foster dependency and subservience in his followers. Such leaders failed to be properly socialized in their youth and carried over into their adult life a need they never learned how to meet. They could have suffered traumatic loss in their past for which they did not heal properly. As a result, they treat people in unhealthy ways to compensate for their own weakness. It is interesting to read about the lives of the founders of high control groups; Many have a strong sense of vulnerability or weakness that they are masking with power or charisma.

Many of the best comedians were very shy and insecure in their youth. Their comedic front was a cover for their insecurity and the means for them to feel significant and accepted. Perhaps for spiritually abusive leaders a similar, but traumatic or damaging, experience in their youth gave rise to the tendency to control and manipulate others and in this way meet their need. *Spiritual abuse is the attempt by the abuser to meet a legitimate need using illegitimate means.*

Because the desire to control others is a human weakness, the problem of spiritual abuse has a long history. It is addressed in both the Old and New Testaments and has a prominent place in the gospels, though not by name.

Spiritual abuse is a modern term that entered our vocabulary in the early '90's. Since 1990 numerous books and websites have been put forward to address it, as well. However, because the desire to control others is a human weakness, the problem of spiritual abuse has a long history. It is addressed in both the Old and New Testaments and has a prominent place in the gospels, though not by name.

Long before the Pharisees, the leaders of God's people abused their authority. Ezekiel describes the basic elements of spiritual abuse—the abuse of power and influence for selfish purposes.

> *"Woe, shepherds of Israel who have been feeding themselves! Should not the shepherds feed the flock? You eat the fat and clothe yourselves with the wool, you slaughter the fat sheep without feeding the flock. Those who are sickly you have not strengthened, the diseased you have not healed, the broken you have not bound up, the scattered you have not brought back, nor have you sought for the lost; but with force and with severity you have dominated them."*
>
> Ezekiel 34:2-4

In scripture, spiritual abuse and legalism are more frequently called *bondage to men*, or *the traditions of men*. It is a by-product and outgrowth of legalism, which is *a preoccupation with the letter of the law without the spirit of the law.*

Jeremiah 5:26-31 describes a perversion of justice in Israel in which those in authority were adding to their own wealth, power, and prestige at the expense of the needy. This angered God and He asked, "*Shall I not punish these people?*" This same perversion of justice is described again in Jeremiah 6:13-14 where false leaders give lip service to healing, saying, "*Peace, peace, but there is no peace.*" Needy people left these spiritual authorities after receiving no real help and God was angry for that. An **authoritarian** leader will seek to be unaccountable for his actions, but God is watching. The best solution for such leaders is that their followers hold them accountable. God said that would not happen because, "*My people love it so!*" (6:31)

Mark 3 describes Jesus entering a synagogue on the Sabbath and encountering a man with a withered hand. The Pharisees watched to see what Jesus would do. They must have felt threatened (or offended), by Jesus' regard for a needy person at the expense of their rules. Jesus saw and knew they would try to accuse Him of "working" on the Sabbath. He also knew that He was going to heal the man, so He used a question to set up the Pharisees to be seen as the hypocrites they were. He asked, "***Is it lawful on the Sabbath to do good or to do harm, to save a life, or to kill?***"

The potential answers to this question for the Pharisees present unacceptable dilemmas. It is like the question, "Have you stopped beating your wife?" It is certainly not lawful to do evil or kill on the Sabbath, which left the Pharisees with just one other choice. That choice pitted the Pharisees against their own traditions and interpretation of the Law. Jesus also knew they wanted to kill Him when He included the reference to killing in His question. That is exactly what the Pharisees began plotting to do when they left.

There is a lesson in this passage for anyone dealing with an abusive religious system. If you challenge, disagree, oppose, or in any way offend, you cannot leave with your reputation intact. In the most severe mind control groups, you may even lose your life, as Jesus did.

Despite the danger Jesus gradually increased the strength of His words and actions against the religious rulers. From His denunciations of the Pharisees, to the cleansing of the Temple, Jesus confronted those who misused their spiritual authority at the expense of those who followed them. A review of two passages will illustrate this.

Luke 15:1,2 displays the attitude of the Pharisees about Jesus' relationship with Publicans and sinners. Jesus dared to share a meal with them; the Pharisees conclude that Jesus must not care about his own spiritual purity if He associates with people of such low moral character. A chasm really did exist between the lowly sinner who knew he was a sinner, and the self-righteous Pharisee. The religious leaders demanded people rise to a level of respectability before they would accept them. **Perfectionism** is a denial of grace. God, however, will come to you and meet you where you are.

Matthew 23 shows Jesus telling the Pharisees they have seated themselves in "Moses's seat," the position of authority, and command things they themselves will not do. They bind heavy burdens on people but will not carry the loads themselves. Jesus then goes on to utter seven "Woes" on the Pharisees for their hypocrisy. He calls them "hypocrites," "whited sepulchers," "serpents," and more. Humble sinners were attracted to Jesus, who was caring and straight-talking. The Pharisees were all facade.

Jesus publicly tells the Pharisees they are **unbalanced** in their weighting of issues. Judgment, mercy, and faith are given insufficient weight, but a tithe on the produce from their garden plots is paid with precise measure. In the Old Testament a tithe was only required on agricultural products. The Pharisees did not derive their income from agriculture, so they were not required to pay a tithe on any other source of income. However, with their garden plots, they legalistically paid a tithe on the tiny amount of produce. (The tithe was not carried over to the New Covenant though cheerful and generous giving certainly is taught in 2nd Corinthians 9:7)

Jesus said the Pharisees strained out gnats but swallowed whole camels. They lacked judgment and mercy and they devoured widows' houses. However, they did pay tithes! They were skilled at applying the letter of the Law to every life situation but had lost the spirit of the Law along the way. This was why the people were alienated from them, and fearful. Jesus illustrated the balance between the spirit and the letter and found a ready reception of His ministry.

If you are recovering from abuse, then you may have felt the appeal of Jesus' gracious forgiveness as you read this. It is His desire to strengthen and build the believer, not condemn. Let Him.

QUESTIONS

1. Were you aware of these examples of spiritual abuse in the Bible?

2. How does God's attitude, expressed in these passages, affect your thinking about Him?

THE CHARACTERISTICS OF SPIRITUAL ABUSE

"A lie is like a snowball: the further you roll it the bigger it becomes."
Martin Luther

It is noteworthy to acknowledge that legalism is the foundation for any abusive system. No grace-based group would regularly practice spiritual abuse. Such abuse arises from the desire to control, which is also at the heart of legalism. When leaders resort to unbiblical methods of leadership the signs are straightforward and easy to spot.

CHARACTERISTICS OF SPIRITUAL ABUSE

- **Authoritarian**
- **Excessive loyalty demands**
- **Facade**
- **Perfectionistic**
- **Unbalanced**
- **Secretive**
- **Paranoid**
- **Labeling others**
- **No accountability**
- **"Friendly fire" casualties**

AUTHORITARIAN

Spiritual abusers are **authoritarian.** Because they are also legalists, the system they lead is characterized by a power structure unaccountable to those who follow. The leader may have a governing board, but he handpicks the members. In such a system the "authority" is never wrong. Fear and intimidation are used to shame those who voice disagreement.

QUESTION

- Have you observed authoritarianism express itself in your group?

EXCESSIVE LOYALTY DEMANDS

There is **excessive loyalty** given to the leaders or the group. They are taught that God anoints the leadership, and the followers are to submit in anything leadership requires. It is also taught that God will bless that submission even if the leader is wrong. In some groups there are tests of loyalty. Proving one's loyalty is a way to rise higher in the esteem of the group or its leader. Failing to prove one's loyalty will place you at the bottom of the group's hierarchy and you will be used as an object lesson.

QUESTIONS

1. Was excessive loyalty expected from you and others in your group? Describe it.

2. Were there any loyalty "tests" to meet? Describe them.

FACADE

It's all a facade. Just like the enablers in the family of an alcoholic that covers the evidence of addiction, so the high control group will hide the hypocrisy, abuse, immorality, and even illegality. The reasoning is that these problems are temporary, or they are acceptable at some level because of the "great good" that is being accomplished by the leader, or group.

QUESTION

- How did the group conceal what they did not want known?

PERFECTIONISTIC

They are perfectionists. High control groups prosper on the labors of their followers. So, perfectionism (works righteousness) is a handy tool to keep the followers busily working out their salvation. "Progress" is more easily measured and reported. The group or its leader usually benefits from this labor.

QUESTION

- Did the group try to keep you busy pursuing a "works" righteousness? How?

UNBALANCED

Spiritual abusers are unbalanced. They focus on things that are minor and blow them out of proportion. Just like the Pharisees who tithed from their small garden plots but neglected the weightier issues of judgment, mercy, and faith, so too these false spiritual leaders will exploit some minor issue to make the group or themselves seem to be ahead of the religious crowd and better than the rest.

QUESTION

- What minor doctrines or practices did the group emphasize?

SECRETIVE

Abusive groups are secretive. Secrets are only legitimate in matters of personal confidentiality. This is an example of one's personal boundaries that can only be crossed with permission. Secrets are not legitimate when there is something unethical, immoral, illegal, or disrespectful that is being concealed. High control groups have a lot of secret sins that must not be discussed.

One tactic used to prevent secrets from becoming public is to teach the doctrine of "touching not the Lord's anointed." If you can cause the followers to think that their words, questions, and even their thoughts are sin when they involve the leaders' activities, then you have effectively stifled the flow of information. It is the freedom to think about other viewpoints and speak freely that abusive leaders fear most. Secrets must be maintained by threat of God's judgment.

QUESTION

- Did your group have any secrets they did not want outsiders to know about? What were they?

PARANOID

Abusers are paranoid. This is a logical necessity given that the group is operating on the dark side of religion. As it says in John chapter 3, "*Men loved the darkness rather than the light; for their deeds were evil.*" False spiritual leaders are paranoid about the possibility that the light will expose their deeds. When paranoid leaders hear someone is asking questions about certain things, they will confront them to make sure they stop. Many times, the rules are unspoken, but if you are in the system for very long you pick up on certain things that are not to be discussed.

QUESTIONS

1. What topics were out of bounds for members to discuss?

2. What topics were kept from outsiders?

LABELING

Troublemakers are labeled. When someone breaks a rule in the group, they are labeled as a trouble-maker, sower of discord, under the control of Satan, or demonized. It doesn't matter what the label is because now the label is being sent away, not a person. Labeling reduces the person to a thing that must be dealt with. To leave the individual's personhood intact is to leave them with a level of respect from the leadership. That then allows the membership to respect them as the person they have always known. When they carry a label, the members disregard the person behind it.

QUESTIONS

1. Were you labeled? What was the label?

2. Do you know of others who were labeled? Describe.

NO ACCOUNTABILITY

There is no accountability. The polity, or system of church government, may exist to provide an accountability structure but it is completely ignored. Or the group has no written polity. In either case, anyone who would dare to question beliefs, or bring a charge against a leader or a favored person within the group must be ready to endure a firestorm of criticism and discipline. In Matthew 18:15-17 there is a process provided for confronting a person who has sinned. Step one, going privately to confront your brother, and step two, going again with a witness, are possible within the abusive system. However, the leaders will prohibit the last step of taking the offender to the whole church.

Many abuse victims have an intense desire to bring their abusers to account. If that is your intention you will need the support of wise advisors. You may also need to think outside the box for creative ways to accomplish your goal. There are ways this has been accomplished but there are real difficulties involved as well.

QUESTION

- What would it require to hold the abusers accountable?

"FRIENDLY FIRE" CASUALTIES

"**Friendly fire casualties abound**." There are a lot of what the military calls friendly fire casualties (when a soldier is accidentally wounded by his comrades). Crossing the leaders, asking questions, disagreeing with the group's pet doctrines, not giving enough, or working hard enough, and a host of other things can bring down that so-called "friendly fire." People who endure such wounds frequently exit the group. They are called "walkaways." Or they are expelled. Some others actually stay in the group and internalize the pain. The alternatives are too stark for them. Leaving may be seen as turning one's back on God and salvation. Rather than forsaking one's salvation or leaving the will of God, some accept the pain and endure it.

QUESTIONS

1. Do you consider yourself a "friendly fire casualty"? Why?

2. Are you aware of others? Describe.

3. Which characteristics of spiritual abuse did you find in your group?

My Personal Journal

"When the ten heard about this, they were indignant with the two brothers. Jesus called them together and said, You know that the rulers of the Gentiles lord it over them, and their high officials exercise authority over them. Not so with you. Instead, whoever wants to become great among you must be your servant, and whoever wants to be first must be your slave, just as the Son of Man did not come to be served, but to serve, and to give his life as a ransom for many."

Matthew 20:20-28

2

The Abusers

"Some men never feel small, but these are the few men who are."
G.K. Chesterton

It is very important to understand the source and cause of spiritual abuse. It's also very important to understand that there is an intersection between religious dysfunction and Christian responsibility. To understand the first is to recognize the necessity for the second. Abusers can only survive when their abuse is allowed.

The Apostle Paul said,

> *"But the Spirit explicitly says, that in later times some will fall away from the faith, paying attention to deceitful spirits and doctrines of demons, by means of the hypocrisy of liars seared in their own conscience as with a branding iron, men who forbid marriage and advocate abstaining from foods, ..."*
>
> I Timothy 4:1-3

What would be the case today if the founders of some of the major cults had been taught, corrected and admonished in a respectful way about the errors they were embarking on when they first began their religious explorations? This same question has been posed about Mao Tse Tung, founder of Chinese communism. Having spent some of his youth in a Christian environment, what might have happened if he had been reached for Christ instead of Marx?

It is quite possible that most cultic leaders, and many converts to cultism, were opportunities lost for the gospel. Though we cannot know or control the hearts of people who become involved in heresy, we can, and should, seek to rescue such people before they seal their commitment to error. This is what Paul refers to I Timothy 4:1 as *"paying attention to deceitful spirits and doctrines of demons."*

Abusers can only survive when their abuse is allowed.

There are warning signs of departure from the faith and into imbalance or abuse. We must first understand why someone would be drawn toward error or the abuse of others. Do they do so consciously or willfully? Perhaps a few religious charlatans like Elmer Gantry consciously choose this path but most make their choice without a full grasp of what is going on. In the words of scripture, they are giving heed to seducing spirits. They are drawn by something attractive to them.

THE THREE MOTIVATIONS: POWER, PRESTIGE, AND THE PURSE

There are three areas of legitimate human need and desire that often are not met sufficiently, at least by the measure of the one feeling the need, or quickly enough to satisfy. If the needs are unmet the temptation may be to fulfill them by an illegitimate means. These three areas include the sense of being in control, having significance, and having money. Let's call them Power, Prestige, and the Purse. These are the root motivations out of which flow behavior patterns of misuse of power, seeking prestige, and coveting money.

The Bible gives many characteristics of mature Christian leaders and the attitudes of followers. However, it also gives us the characteristics of the dysfunctional leader and his blind followers. The examples found in Scripture are always found among those who are out of balance in the three areas of Power, Prestige and the Purse. They are illustrated graphically in both the Old and New Testaments, but especially in Matthew 23. Let's look at this in some depth.

THE ABUSE OF POWER

The "power" of spiritual leaders in the Bible is that of godly and humble influence, not coercive power. It is to lead and guide, not push. When things don't go as a dysfunctional leader wants, he may resort to coercive means. The urge to control is a strong one, especially among insecure people who lack faith in God and, therefore, resort to the use of various control mechanisms.

Jesus said:

> *"But be not ye called Rabbi: for one is your Master, even Christ; and all ye are brethren.... Neither be ye called masters: for one is your Master, even Christ"*
>
> Matthew 23:8,10.

If Christians are all brothers and sisters before God, how can one be a master, or have superior authority over another? Aren't brothers and sisters equal? The Reformation and biblical doctrine of the Priesthood of the Believer is at the heart of this issue. The Priesthood of the Believer holds that every believer is his own priest, and can enter the presence of God, on his own behalf.

Wielding power in an abusive group can enable the leaders to accumulate money and prestige. These three elements are usually found together in abusive leadership.

Control mechanisms where power is exerted may include:

Fear—of God's displeasure for any failure.
Guilt—for failing to live up to the group's standards.
Manipulation—submit to the leader and God will bless you.
Shaming—being labeled as spiritually defective for any offense.

Jesus only resorted to coercive power one time in His earthly ministry when He drove the money-changers out of the temple. These people had corrupted the godly function of the temple for their own selfish use. They abused the people of God and His house, and thus enraged His Son. Today, believers are the Temple of the Holy Spirit. Rest assured that all who defile God's Temple will face His wrath.

QUESTIONS

1. Which of the control mechanisms, (fear, guilt, manipulation, or shaming) did you see employed in your group?

2. Describe how they were used.

THE ABUSE OF PRESTIGE

Every person wants to feel that his life is significant. This is legitimate. The perversion of this, however, is when the appearance of significance is more important than the substance. It is a gross exaggeration like the Wizard of Oz who is really just "the little man behind the curtain."

Prestige is a commodity that can be used to obtain power and/or money. We see this frequently among politicians and activists in the secular arena, but it also occurs in the spiritual arena.

The dysfunctional leader may seek to "sit in Moses' seat"—the seat of authority from God (Matthew 23:2),—and to be seen as a "channel" through which unquestionable words pass. The implication is that his words are God's words and must be obeyed without question. Because of the corrupt motivation in the heart of such a leader a façade of righteousness will become the inevitable result.

Jesus said of the Pharisees:

> *"But all their deeds to be noticed by men; for they broaden their phylacteries, and lengthen the tassels of their garments, and they love the place of honor at banquets, and the chief seats in the synagogues, And respectful greetings in the market places, and being called of men Rabbi."*
>
> Matthew 23:5-7

And again,

> *"Woe unto you, scribes and Pharisees, hypocrites! For you clean the outside of the cup and of the dish, but inside they are full of bribery and self indulgence"*
>
> Matthew 23:25

Once false prestige is achieved, any criticism or questioning will be treated as a cheap attack on a great man of God. The dysfunctional leader will use his status to prevent criticism. He will elevate those who agree with him and demote, or eliminate, dissenters, thus presenting a solid front of the leadership to the followers. (See also Galatians 6:12,13)

Some of the characteristics common to false prestige include:

Elitism—set themselves apart from the common man, preferring the company of other elites.
Appearance is Everything—a hypocritical disconnect between reality and how things appear.
Unquestionable—self-important status places them above question.

QUESTIONS

1. Did the leader of your group seem to revel in his prestige?

2. How was it expressed?

3. How did it affect you and others?

THE ABUSE OF THE PURSE

Money is a medium of exchange for most things obtainable in life. A minister, like any other person, may seek it for its proper uses. It is not seeking money that is the problem but loving it. The *love of money*, not money itself, is the root of all evil (I Timothy 6:10). Money is a medium of exchange that can be used to obtain power and prestige.

Scripture has some clear things to say about the abuse of money:

> *"For there are many rebellious men, empty talkers and deceivers, especially those of the circumcision, who must be silenced because they are upsetting whole families, teaching things they should not teach, for the sake of sordid gain."*
>
> Titus 1:10, 11

> *"And in their greed they will exploit you with false words; their judgment from long ago is not idle, and their destruction is not asleep.".*
>
> 2 Peter 2:3

Something remarkably consistent among most cults is their wealth and preoccupation with it. Ostensibly the money is for the furthering of the influence of the group and its message, but somehow the leadership enjoys a lot of it, too. One cult leader lives on a palatial estate in New York. Another enjoyed a mansion in California with a $9,600 Cadillac during the Depression. Many other examples could be cited. Spiritual leaders don't have to live in poverty but there shouldn't be a significant disconnect between them and the people they lead, especially if they are asking for financial sacrifices by the followers.

Most cults teach Old Testament tithing, as a compulsory way to increase income, but not all. One large cult emphasizes the point that it doesn't pass a collection plate or require tithing. However, this cult receives vast sums of money from other sources. One heretical movement teaches that a sign of spirituality is that you have financial success, and the sign of lack of faith is a financial struggle. The members of another extremely wealthy cult jokingly refer to tithing as "fire insurance." The only cult in church history to repent of its false doctrines and become orthodox also quit requiring a triple tithe. This group demonstrated their sincerity when they de-emphasized money, and it is that de-emphasis that is the important point. Splinters from this group who did not go along with the reformation continue to require the triple tithe. In contrast Jesus knew Judas was a thief but let him handle the money anyway. He was not focused on money. He focused on His ministry and trusted His Father to provide.

Common characteristics of financial imbalance include:

Buy a Blessing—or promises of material blessing for financial sacrifice to the group.
Shell Games—or difficulty ascertaining financial integrity.
Burdensome—those who cannot afford it are shamed for robbing God and manipulated into financial sacrifice.
Devourer—the leader is "well off" at the expense of the needy.

Paul said, *"Be imitators of me, just as I also am of Christ"* (I Corinthians 11:1). Paul implied that if he ceased to follow Christ, then Christians should cease following him. A healthy environment includes both a two-way accountability and openness of the leader, and discernment by the followers.

The correction for the imbalance of Power, Prestige or the Purse is a genuine and effective two-way accountability between leadership and informed, discerning followers. When the followers do not inform themselves and think critically, they are abdicating the role God intended for them and choosing to remain spiritual children, dependent on their leaders.

QUESTIONS

1. How was money dealt with in your group?

2. Was there a preoccupation with it?

3. What was the income or lifestyle of the leader, contrasted with that of the members?

My Personal Journal

"Woe to the shepherds who are destroying and scattering the sheep of my pasture!" declares the LORD. Therefore, this is what the LORD, the God of Israel, says to the shepherds who tend my people: Because you have scattered my flock and driven them away and have not bestowed care on them, I will bestow punishment on you for the evil you have done, declares the LORD."

Jeremiah 23:1-4

3

Who Joins Abusive Groups?

"Most modern freedom is at root fear.
It is not so much that we are too bold to endure rules;
it is rather that we are too timid to endure responsibilities."
G.K. Chesterton

The question of who joins high control religious groups seems like it would have a simple answer. It does not. Nor is there a simple answer to how it happens.

The starting place should be the question of what disposes a person to spiritual abuse? Why is a person vulnerable? What differences in people make one vulnerable and another not so vulnerable? Here is a list that may help you think it through.

Which of these statements fit you?

1. I had a lack of knowledge of the Bible.
2. I was raised in an abusive family or church, so I didn't know the difference.
3. I was not sufficiently strong in critical thinking skills or will power.
4. I came to Christ through the abusive group's influence.
5. I was like the frog in the kettle where error came so gradually, I didn't notice until it was too late.
6. I am easily led, or I want someone to take the lead for me.
7. (Something else?) Explain:

ABUSED PEOPLE SHARE THEIR REASONS FOR INVOLVEMENT:

First Person, gave two answers:

> ***Fear***—*Fearful of missing God so you do EVERYTHING the person you consider to be the authority tells you. (for example GIVE, GIVE, GIVE)*

Feeling of Spiritual Inadequacy*—Feeling that others are more spiritual so they must have ALL the knowledge. Feeling like you "blew it" so you need others to help you see truth etc.*

Second Person said:

"I think that one big one, at least for me, is that I had no idea that a Pastor or Church would do such a thing to the very people they claim to care so much about. I, for one, thought that even though you may differ on some Biblical issues, basically the church I was a member of was a safe place. Church does not hurt people. It is supposed to be a place where you are loved, cared for, able to grow up in the Lord Jesus Christ. A place where you are not harmed, spiritually or mentally. I think that another one might be closely related to the person's past, also the abuser's past as well."

Third Person said:

"Being a compliant child, and having a need to be accepted and validated."

Fourth Person said:

"Of your reasons that people get involved in a cult--I think all of those reasons could apply to my ex-husband. But the one that applies to me is the gradually-getting-worse idea. And I also think that none of us wants to think that anyone is 'bad' or 'abusive'. We [Christians] try and rationalize people's behavior and don't want to think of them negatively. We WANT to live in peace."

Having good insight into one's vulnerability is an indication that the person is no longer vulnerable in that area. Like scar tissue now there is strength where there was once a wound. This awareness of vulnerability is vital in recovering from abuse. It is one thing to know that abuse happened, that it was abuse, and that the guilt resides in the abuser, but it is another thing entirely to know why you were a victim. If that lesson is not learned, and it frequently is not, then another round of abuse is possible.

People who were raised in families where dysfunction was the norm may gravitate toward a church that is like their family of origin. It's all they know. It's the familiar rut with an accepted comfort level. The way to break out of such a rut is exposure to a much more gracious culture. Hopefully the contrast will stir a hunger for grace and not performance. This is what the people in the Bible who knew they were sinners saw in Jesus. They contrasted Him to the self-righteous Pharisees and knew instantly that Jesus was someone to listen to.

> *It is one thing to know that something bad happened, that it was abuse, and that guilt resides with the abuser, but it is another thing entirely to know why you were a victim.*

Some people who have been raised in dysfunctional families grow up with a shame-based identity. These individuals think, "I am defective," or, "I am not worthy of respect." It is easy to get such a person to accept blame, or to submit to a strong-willed leader. He or she needs help to cultivate a stronger sense of self-respect and boundaries.

I had a conversation years ago with a pastor who acknowledged that legalism was a problem in his church. I suggested he preach on grace in contrast to performance, as a way to open the eyes of the legalists and those with a shame-based identity to their need of a gracious spirituality. He reacted defensively, as if I had accused him of not preaching grace. I assured him that was not what was meant. I described a message that would outline what grace would say about this and that, and in contrast, what a performance-based relationship with God would say on the same things.

The problem for the legalist is that he can hear a message on grace and think he must perform better. By putting the two mindsets together in contrast the legalist can see the difference and be better equipped to understand the fundamental difference grace will make.

BOOMERANG BELIEVERS

In my years of dealing with cults and abusive groups I have noticed that people who have been involved with controlling systems and have left for some reason tend to return to very similar groups. It would seem logical that the response would be to get as far away from such abusive control as possible. Though that is one of the reactions, it is not necessarily the most common one.

Many years ago, I frequently encountered a man at the Post Office while picking up my mail. He was a member of one of the large cults. Let's call it Cult #1. We would talk and I would offer tracts to him that dealt with this particular cult. One day he called me over to tell me he was no longer a member of Cult #1. My first question was "Well, what are you now?" His answer shocked me. He said, "I joined Cult #2" (Actually he didn't say that but remember I am not naming any groups so you will have to use your imagination.) I suggested he had jumped out of the frying pan and into the fire. I then began offering him tracts on Cult #2. Twenty years later I got a call from him and heard him say he had finally left Cult #2 and had become a Christian because of some of the things I had warned him about regarding some bizarre doctrines of Cult #2. He had finally seen it. God was faithful. But why did he turn from one controlling group to another?

People tend to gravitate toward the familiar. That is human nature. It's not necessarily good or bad. It's our comfort zone. Most of our "thinking" is not necessarily conscious reasoning. We can think emotionally at a deep subconscious level that does not rise to the level of conscious awareness. For instance, when we experience an emotionally traumatic injury we may never get to the rational conscious level where we weigh the factors and arrive at an understanding of our motivations. We act in response to our emotional need. Consider this statement from *Passages of Marriage* by Minirth, Newman, and Hemfelt:

> *"... a curious phenomenon... counselors see constantly. That is, the more dysfunctional and unsatisfying a child's family of origin has been, the harder it is for the child to leave it. Logic suggests that if the original family failed to serve that person's needs, leaving home is the solution. But human beings do not operate on logic. More than*

80 percent of our decisions are made below the conscious level, in the deep recesses of thought and sub-thought where logic never goes."[1]

There is something appealing to those worn ruts in our life, even when they don't help us.

People who have been on the treadmill of legalism and spiritual abuse can find it difficult to break away and move into a healthy environment. They may be trapped between that sub-conscious level of thinking and some assumptions about God and biblical truth that hold them in bondage.

People who have been on the treadmill of legalism and spiritual abuse can find it difficult to break away and move into a healthy environment.

BREAKING THE BONDAGE

First, the person must recognize the nature of his bondage. He must understand that the legalism and abuse he has experienced is far beyond the bounds of what the Bible teaches. When I help someone exit an abusive group, I start by listing the characteristics of legalism and spiritual abuse. This helps demonstrate a pattern and system involved. To hear it described as it really is shows it to be more sinister than it was previously assumed to be.

Second, exit strategies from previous life patterns must be addressed. The person needs to examine the patterns of his own thinking and feeling. What motivates him? What is he seeking? What causes him to choose one thing over another? Why does he return to the familiar rut? Once a person gains this insight about himself, he must learn how to separate his sub-conscious motivations from his rational, conscious, thinking. Many victims of serious abuse, in an emotional knee-jerk reaction, will re-examine everything they ever believed. This can be good, but it can also be dangerous because of the effect of "emotional" thinking as described above.

It is very important to find a grace-filled environment first. This will allow the individual to resolve any other issues in a supportive setting. **Perhaps the most important factor in resolving those other issues is to find a counselor who understands biblical teaching on grace and the many lesser doctrines that were misused to manipulate and control the person in the past. Also, a licensed professional counselor can help identify any self-defeating patterns in one's thinking.**

"I, even I, am He who comforts you, who are you that you are afraid of man who dies, and the son of man who is made like grass?"

Isaiah 51:12

1 Minirth, Newman, and Hemfelt, *Passages of Marriage*, Thomas Nelson, pgs. 23-24

QUESTIONS

1. What reasons have you discerned why you might have been vulnerable to recruitment?

2. How will you go about finding a grace-filled setting for your recovery?

3. What patterns of thinking or attitudes do you need to change?

4. How will you change them?

My Personal Journal

"The Lord is near to the brokenhearted
And saves those who are crushed in spirit"

Psalm 34:18

4

Roles Played in High Control Groups

Of all tyrannies, a tyranny sincerely exercised for the good of it's victims may be the most oppressive.
C.S. Lewis

"For am I now seeking the favor of men, or of God? Or am I striving to please men? If I were still trying to please men, I would not be a bond-servant of Christ."
Galatians 1:10

In high control religious systems everyone plays his or her appointed role. When someone breaks out of their role they fulfill another purpose within the system, an object lesson, which will be used to strengthen the control of the leadership.

ROLES PLAYED

These players are called the Tyrant, the Henchmen, the Silent Sheep, the Wounded and the Dissident. As you read their descriptions think of who modeled the role in your own experience. It needs to be said here that the second through fifth roles can be the same person but at different stages, or times. This will be explained later.

Roles Played

The Tyrant
The Henchmen
The Silent Sheep
The Wounded
The Dissident

The Tyrant is always the head of the organization or group. Frequently he is the founder. There is usually a cult of personality, or an adulation of the leader. He is not open to criticism or disagreement. He will not put up with anyone who might compete with him. Though he seems extremely confident, he is really an insecure person who has compensated through the use of power, fear, manipulation, guilt, and intimidation. Anyone who opposes him in any way must be sent away or run off, usually with their reputation in tatters.

The Henchmen. The Tyrant relies on this second level of leadership to monitor and control the group. The Henchmen get their sense of reward or fulfillment by pleasing the Tyrant. In a cult of personality, the closer you are to that central person, the more prestige and power you have. Thus, the Henchmen will do the dirty work for the tyrant. They will enforce the group's rules by the methods prescribed by the Tyrant, which is usually the use of manipulation, intimidation, fear, guilt, and the threat of ostracism.

The Silent Sheep The dysfunctional system has enablers much like that of the family of an alcoholic. You've probably seen images of the three monkeys who "see no evil, hear no evil, and speak no evil." Like them, the Silent Sheep fear to rock the boat. They lack the confidence that what they see, hear, or think could be true. In high control groups the leaders want followers like little children who have not learned enough or had enough life experience to have confidence in their own judgment. Silent Sheep invariably defer to the views of their leaders. They have a "learned powerlessness." Because they will not speak up, they also think they are alone in their views and do not know that many have also observed the same things.

However, these Silent Sheep can become very vocal when defending the group to outsiders, or against those they view as apostates. When they become vocal in their defense, they are called Loyalists. Their world is very insecure. Within the group they fear the insecurity they might create if they express their thoughts. To outsiders who criticize the group they will strenuously defend their unreal world lest it become insecure.

The Wounded. This person has crossed the line in some way that brought down the ire of the Tyrant or one of his Henchmen. He or she has been marked by the group for humiliating treatment. In a dysfunctional group, this person serves as an example to demonstrate that the Tyrant will follow through with a public humiliation, so others will fear to speak their minds or question him. The Wounded individual is in great self-doubt and may have internalized the false guilt the system has imposed.

If you are one of the Wounded, please know that God Himself is angry with those who have put this guilt on you. He demonstrated this in the Gospels when He healed a man born blind and told him to go and wash himself at the pool of Siloam (John 9). The man came into conflict with the religious rulers because his healing was by Jesus, whom the religious leaders feared. Thus, they had to accuse the man in some way. They excommunicated him, or as the Bible says, "They cast him out." Jesus sought him out and introduced Himself as the Son of God, his Savior, and the man worshipped Him. In John 6:37 Jesus said of this type of person, "...the one who comes to me I will certainly not cast out." Jesus will not excommunicate anyone who comes to Him. If Jesus Himself will not cast you out, then don't be afraid of anyone else making such a threat. Don't allow yourself to remain wounded. There is help for you.

The Dissident has seen enough. His conscience has won out and he must speak up. Dissidents tell what they know, and have seen, and they are usually very angry about it because of their own injury, or the injury of someone they love. Anger imparts the courage to overcome a learned powerlessness and take a stand.

The group cannot allow a dissident to speak his or her mind freely. The methods to silence Dissidents will be fear, guilt, intimidation, manipulation, and more. Some groups will even buy the silence of dissidents. If they cannot prevent the dissident from speaking, then they must close the ears of those loyalists in the group who are not yet informed. One thing is frequently true in every group—most dissidents cannot leave the group with their reputation intact.

As said before, different roles can be the played by one person at different stages. I have seen a Henchman who was also a Silent Sheep become a Wounded Dissident almost overnight. This person had been both a Silent Sheep and a Henchman for years. Then, in a short period, his eyes were opened, and the group wounded his reputation and ostracized him.

The Tyrant, on the other hand, seldom ever repents. The Tyrant is like a person who is riding a Tiger; he dares not get off. He is too insecure to face the consequences of letting go of control.

QUESTIONS

1. Who was the Tyrant in your group?

2. Who were the Henchmen?

3. Were there Silent Sheep that you know about?

4. Do you know of any Wounded?

5. Who are the Dissidents?

6. Have you talked to any from these last three categories about their experiences or opinions? What did you learn?

My Personal Journal

"And the word of the Lord came to me, saying, Son of man, prophesy against the shepherds of Israel, prophesy and say to them, Thus says the Lord God to the shepherds: Woe to the shepherds of Israel who feed themselves! Should not the shepherds feed the flocks? You eat the fat and clothe yourselves with the wool; you slaughter the fatlings, but you do not feed the flock. The weak you have not strengthened, nor have you healed those who were sick, nor bound up the broken, nor brought back what was driven away, nor sought what was lost; but with force and cruelty you have ruled them. So, they were scattered because there was no shepherd; and they became food for all the beasts of the field when they were scattered. My sheep wandered through all the mountains, and on every high hill; yes, My flock was scattered over the whole face of the earth, and no one was seeking or searching for them."

Ezekiel 34:1-6

5

Legalism

"The truth is, of course, that the curtness of the Ten Commandments is an evidence, not of the gloom and narrowness of a religion, but, on the contrary, of its liberality and humanity. It is shorter to state the things forbidden than the things permitted: precisely because most things are permitted, and only a few things are forbidden."

G.K. Chesterton

LEGALISM, THE SEEDBED OF HIGH CONTROL

There are three levels of control in any performance-based religion. The first level is legalism. It is the seedbed out of which the other two, spiritual abuse and mind control, grow. When I meet with groups of dissidents from high control groups, I describe the characteristics of each of these three levels. This gives them the information they need to recognize that they were part of a system of control and abuse. The tendency of victims is to assume that they were guilty, unspiritual, had sins for which God was punishing them, or just didn't measure up. After hearing the abuse characteristics described they learn it was the system, not them, and they are freed from false guilt.

BALANCING LAW AND GRACE

"See to it that no one takes you captive through philosophy and empty deception, according to the traditions of men, according to the elementary principles of the world, rather than according to Christ."

Colossians 2:8

To evaluate the issues related to legalism we must consider the balance between Law and Grace, to become aware of how legalism manifests itself, and learn the most common characteristics of legalistic Christianity. You must understand this section to fully appreciate the next section on spiritual abuse. They are related as the root is to the fruit.

For two millennia Christians have wrestled with the balance between God's Law, exemplified by the Ten Commandments and the Old Testament, and the doctrine of grace as exemplified in the New Testament. The Judaizers were among the first to try to mix law and grace and Paul dealt sternly with them in Galatians. Martin Luther, on the other hand, didn't like the Apostle James' comments about faith without works being dead.

Every charlatan and false teacher who wants to accumulate power, prestige, and money will emphasize the believer's obedience and performance to create energy among his followers to produce those outwardly measurable results.

When we see abuses, we naturally wonder where to find the balance between God's Law, which is righteous, and His saving grace, which He says, is "not of works." It can be summed up by saying it is the "direction" we are going, not the "things" we do, or don't do, along the way.

The Old Testament Law was fulfilled on our behalf at Calvary.

First of all, the Old Testament Law was fulfilled on our behalf at Calvary. It was nailed to the cross by Jesus perfect obedience and death on our behalf (Colossians 2:14-17). Being nailed to His cross means that the Law died with Jesus. We are no longer held under the jurisdiction of the Law. If you are driving on the highway in your state and a state trooper from the neighboring state pulls you over for a traffic violation any ticket he issues will be dismissed in court because he is out of his jurisdiction. He is an officer of the law, and the law is just, but he cannot apply it to someone who is not under its jurisdiction.

Because of Christ's fulfillment of the Law on our behalf, we are no longer under its jurisdiction. However, God's Law is just, and we must not dismiss it as being unrelated to our Christian life.

The purpose of the Law was to teach us that 1) We are sinners, 2) We cannot keep the law perfectly, and 3) We need a Deliverer who can resolve our guilt problem. For us as Christians, that purpose has been fulfilled. Several passages in the New Testament describe the relationship of law and faith. Read Romans chapters 3–5, the entire book of Galatians, and Hebrews chapter 7.

The purpose of the Law was to teach us that:

1. **We are sinners**
2. **We cannot keep the law perfectly**
3. **We need a Deliverer who can resolve our guilt problem**

In Christ the Law was kept perfectly. That perfect obedience is credited to our account by faith in Him. In Christ, Who is eternal deity, we find someone Who can absorb all the wrath of God against sin. Therefore, when we place our faith in His atoning death on our behalf, we are redeemed. If we try to add our works, traditions, or any other requirements to His atonement, we say His death was insufficient, that something was lacking in Him. This is an insult to God.

By faith we receive salvation, and our spiritual birth occurs. By that new birth we receive the Holy Spirit, the Spirit of the Law, who then dwells in our hearts. The Holy Spirit is the Law of God written on our hearts. The Law becomes part of our new nature in Christ.

Because the Law is fulfilled in Christ the written Law has been "set aside" (Hebrews 7:18-19). It has lost its force because we are not under its jurisdiction. That does not mean we may disregard it. It still shows us our sin in contrast to Christ's perfection, and so it shows us how great is our salvation. It also shows us the virtues of God's grace, mercy, forbearance, and love toward us. His love for us is the reason why we develop a love for Him. Love will always outperform obligation. How can we then impose the "traditions of men" on others through legalism? To do so is to take on the convicting role of the Holy Spirit.

The Law of God is still a reflection of His will for us. It tells us what He wants us to do or not do. "Thou shalt not kill, steal, bear false witness," etc., are still His will for us. The purpose of the Law is the same as it was in the Old Testament when it had jurisdiction: It is to teach us that we are sinners. There is no loophole we can wiggle through; there is no mitigating circumstance that leaves us innocent. We are taught our thorough sinfulness by the Law as we compare our actions with its standards.

Jesus upped the ante by saying it is not just our actions, but our attitudes, motives, and desires that must be compared to that standard. Paul said the Law was our schoolmaster, or tutor, whose job it was to teach us just how sinful and hopeless we were (Galatians 3:15-29). When we understand that hopelessness, we recognize we need a savior because He has left us no other alternative.

You may have heard preached and taught your entire Christian life lists of things you are to do or not do. How are we to relate to them? Matthew 22:34-40 describes a scene of Jesus vs. the Pharisees. The text says a "lawyer" (wouldn't you know it?) questions Jesus about which law of God was the greatest. Jesus' answer explains our relationship to the Law. He said,

> "You *shall love the Lord your God with all your heart, and with you're your soul, and with all your mind.... The second is like it, You shall love your neighbor as yourself. On these two commandments depend the whole Law and the Prophets."*

Where are the lists of do's and don'ts? Where are the prohibited things? The Ten Commandments are a list of actions to do or not do, but Jesus just summed them up in an attitude, a commitment to love. Genuine love does not need a list of do's and don'ts. The desire to please God arises out of love.

In marriage relationships, love motivates us to do what pleases our spouse. It is written on our hearts. That is what God has done in the New Birth. He has given us His Spirit, the Spirit of the Law, to indwell us, guide us, and correct us. God's Spirit convicts of sin, not some man-made standard supposedly based on the Law.

Legalism is supposedly a zeal for righteousness, the Law, truth, and justice. However, it is overzealous at the expense of the fruit of the Spirit. It tends to the spiritual affairs of others without consideration for gracious virtues; it is unbalanced.

God's Spirit convicts of sin, not some manmade standard based on the Law.

In reality legalism is trusting in oneself, as Jesus said of the Pharisees in Luke 18:9, "*And He also told this parable to certain ones who trusted in themselves that they were righteous, and viewed others with contempt*." Legalism is corrupting in its influence. Paul describes it in Galatians 5:9, "*A little leaven leavens the whole lump of dough*."

The balance between law and grace is found in our relationship with Him. We love Him because He first loved us. We obey Him because we want to please Him (not to escape His wrath, because we are no longer subject to it.) We are free to love Him. That love will resolve the balancing problem. Any other method of balancing law and grace will fail.

Those who have been through the experience of legalism and spiritual abuse have been through a vacuum absent of Christian grace. They were immersed in performance and driven by fear and guilt.

Paul says in Galatians 1 that such a system is *anathema* (accursed of God). If you know the Lord, you are free. Never again let anyone bring you into bondage to performance.

QUESTIONS

1. Was the Law a legalistic list of do's and don'ts used to manipulate or condemn you? How?

2. Explain your understanding of why the Law (though good) can't be used to condemn you.

Genuine love does not need a list of do's and don'ts. The desire to please God arises out of love.

KINDS OF LEGALISM

"A Pharisee is hard on others and easy on himself, but a spiritual man is easy on others and hard on himself."

A.W. Tozer

As you read the characteristics of legalism, make notes. If you are in a group, discuss how each characteristic found an expression in the legalistic group you came from. Find examples that others agree come out of a performance-based understanding of how we relate to God. Examples of legalism should be more than incidental; they should fit a larger pattern. We all say and do things occasionally that could be considered legalistic. But I am describing a pervasive culture, a thoroughgoing attitude of performance.

Legalism is defined in Matthew 15:9, when Jesus is talking about the Pharisees. He says they are *"teaching as doctrines the precepts of men."* Legalism is a man-made extension of the Law of God, a list of rules governing our life, rather than principles. It looks almost exclusively at the outside of a Christian, the part everyone can see, and then judges the heart from that. Only God is able to judge the heart. (*"...man looks at the outward appearance, but the Lord looks at the heart"* 1 Samuel 16:7).

Legalism grows out of an application of the Law to real life situations. In the first generation a problem arises to which a solution is sought from scripture. A "rule" is made that will govern the situation. In the second generation the times have changed, and the rule needs to be updated by going back to the principle governing the situation. This seldom happens because in that time frame the principle has been forgotten and the rule "was good enough for my parents so it's good enough for you." The third generation usually rebels at such rules because they are unreasonable and ill founded.

Living in a performance-based relationship with God is what legalism produces. It also produces spiritual burnout.

Harold Bussell wrote in his book *Unholy Devotion,*

> "Central to all biblical instruction is our responsibility to make right choices. We are free to make any choice, but we are not called to act on every freedom. On occasion we must place voluntary restrictions on ourselves. Selected restrictions do not make us legalists. We become legalistic only when we begin to define mature Christianity on the basis of these restrictions and when we use them as a means for accepting other Christians into our fellowship or excluding them from it."[2]

THREE EXPRESSIONS OF LEGALISM

Salvation by works. Paul addresses this expression of legalism in Galatians. We try to complete Christ's work on Calvary by our holy living, as if Christ's death is not quite enough and He needs us to finish the deal with God. Paul questions this by asking in Galatians 3:3; *"Having begun by the Spirit, are you now being perfected by the flesh?"*

<u>Such doctrines as the following deny salvation is by grace through faith alone:</u>

- Baptismal regeneration—salvation is complete only after baptism.
- Salvation evidenced by speaking in tongues—anyone who does not, is not saved.
- Worshipping on a specific day to be righteous.
- Pelagianism—saying "faith without works is dead" to generate behavior. (Paul called it anathema.)

2 Harold Bussell, *Unholy Devotion*, Zondervan, page 80

All the world's religions teach a form of salvation by works. Christianity is alone in saying there is nothing you can do to be saved but to receive it by faith apart from your works. (Ephesians 2:8-9)

Inward Legalism. This is an introspective search for a sense of approval by God, self and others by reaching or maintaining a level of spiritual performance. This unconscious effort may go back to childhood where parental approval was conditional. In adulthood the individual thinks that after having been saved, he or she needs to keep God's favor or grace through spiritual performance. To fall below that standard is to lose His love and acceptance. The person may take on a heavy load of responsibility in the group, so they feel good about themselves, or to win the approval of the group or its leader. Any failure of performance leads to a false sense of shame and guilt, and a feeling of being unspiritual. This performance standard originated with man, not God; the individual, the group, or its leader has substituted himself in the place of the Holy Spirit to convict of sin.

Outward Legalism. This includes a dogmatic assertion of personal convictions as if they were the will of God for every believer. Social and doctrinal matters are precisely defined and enforced, individual liberty is greatly reduced, and the group begins to live like modern-day Pharisees. Jesus described it in Matthew 23:27 as "*whitewashed tombs*."

For example:

- Social standards that require specific styles of dress and grooming.
- A list of forbidden activities.
- Holding doctrinal positions that in church history would be considered secondary, or less essential to the faith.

There needs to be a balance in the Body of Christ between being mutually accountable to biblical standards and assuming our interpretation of those standards is the only correct one. The individual must listen first to scripture and his conscience, then the opinions of others who are mature in the faith.

Many standards assumed to have their basis in scripture have been influenced by our culture. The first church controversy in Acts 15 describes the church at Antioch, which was made up of both Gentile and Jewish Christians. The Jews had cultural taboos (especially regarding food and diet) that had built up over the centuries of living under the Old Testament law. The Gentiles had no taboo about eating unbled meat, or meat offered to idols. When they brought this food to the "church supper" the response of the Jews led to a division in the church.

Paul took the issue to Jerusalem, and the solution was a compromise that held for that particular group in that place at that time. Paul later said in I Corinthians 8:9-13, if our conscience does not of-

All the world's religions teach a form of salvation by works. Christianity is alone in saying there is nothing you can do to be saved but to receive it by faith apart from your works. (Ephesians 2:8-9)

fend, we may eat meat offered to idols. Thus, the ruling at Acts 15 was a local and temporary compromise and not a ruling for all Christians everywhere.

Living in a performance-based relationship with God is what legalism produces. It also produces spiritual burnout. When the expected blessings do not come after our strenuous effort we lose faith in God, in His Word and in ourselves. At this point we ask ourselves, "What's the use?" and leave it all behind for a life in "spiritual limbo" where we are still Christians but not in fellowship with God or His Church.

Jesus said in John 14:15, "*If you love me, you will keep my commandments.*" As you read that verse, on which phrase did you focus - "keeping the commandments" or "loving Jesus?" If you focus on loving Jesus keeping commandments will be light. It is very much like the many things we do for a loved one. They are not heavy if we are motivated by love. In contrast, consider what Jesus said in Matthew 11:28. "*Come to me all who are weary and are heavy-laden, and I will give you rest.*" The meaning of the Greek word translated "heavy-laden" is *Phortizo*, meaning "to overburden with spiritual anxiety."[3] That is exactly how someone feels who thinks that God loves them more or less based on their performance. Jesus is saying, "If you are burdened down with religious performance, come to Me and I will give you rest."

QUESTIONS

1. How was legalism part of your experience?

2. Was your focus Inward or Outward in its emphasis? Explain.

3. Did your group teach salvation by works? Explain.

3 Augustus Strong, *Strongs Exhaustive Concordance*, MacDonald Publishing Co. Greek Dictionary—definition #5412

4. Have you sought biblical answers for these issues? What have you discovered?

CHARACTERISTICS OF LEGALISM

"Beware of false prophets, who come to you in sheep's clothing, but inwardly are ravenous wolves. You will know them by their fruits."

Matthew 7:15

LEGALISTS ARE POSITION CONSCIOUS

Modern legalists make much of their position of authority, their title, their degree. Even if they don't outwardly emphasize their position, they may hold to a concept called *delegated authority*, or a *chain of command*. This concept holds that God has given His authority to spiritual leaders and will hold them accountable for their use of it. Those under authority of these earthly leaders must submit as if to God Himself. Even if the leader is wrong, this teaching says, you will please God by following him. God will correct the leader, not you.

This doctrine came into American Christianity through books written by Watchman Nee, a Chinese Christian leader who reflected his cultural values in his Christian teaching. This teaching of delegated authority is actually derived from Confucian teaching which so permeated Chinese culture that Nee just assumed it, though it clearly violates scripture in many places.

When the legalistic leader is challenged, or crossed in any way, he will invariably resort to asserting his authority. Persuasion, teaching, and gracious forbearance are not in his repertoire of responses.

QUESTION

- How did you see Position Consciousness expressed in your group?

LEGALISTS ARE CONFORMISTS

Legalists are not tolerant of nonconformists. Such a person demonstrates personal independence, which poses a problem for their regimented system. To tolerate someone who thinks and acts independently or differently is to be weak. It would compromise God's truth to not speak out against such a person.

Hair and dress styles are big indicators to legalists as to where your heart is. If your hair is not groomed according to their standard, you must be worldly or a rebel. Certain habits and activities are forbidden to a "real" Christian; you can compile a long list with some groups.

As conformists' legalists are also inflexible. They can only think, act and be what the group dictates. To do otherwise is to become a compromiser, (a feared term among them). In healthy groups exposure to diversity makes a person think about his assumptions, ask himself questions, and deal with his prejudices. But uniformity will destroy critical thinking and harden wrong beliefs and prejudices. Spiritual form will ultimately replace spiritual vitality.

Legalists are captured by the culture of their group. They are under more severe peer pressure than anyone else in the public. They dare not cross the boundaries of what is acceptable to the group; to question is to be disrespectful or disloyal. There is an unwritten rule in place governing such things. Jeff VanVonderen calls it the "Can't Talk" rule. You only know it exists when you violate it.

Legalism is about behaviors and focuses on externals.

Legalism is about behaviors and focuses on externals. It is preoccupied with **performance,** and this leads to perfectionism. The more "perfect" you can be, the more pleasing you are to God and the group. Being able to verify and control external spiritual performance helps legalists feel secure. Appearance is everything to them in contradiction to 1st Samuel 16:7:

> *"man looks at the outward appearance, but the Lord looks at the heart"*

The ultimate problem with a performance-based relationship with God is that it depends on you. You get on the pathway to God thinking you will walk for a time and then check your progress. When you stop beside the path to check your progress you discover the scenery has not changed; everything is as it was when you began. So, you get back on the pathway to God and begin to jog. You think perhaps that you were not giving yourself to the task sufficiently. After a while, you feel the need to check your progress but again the scenery has not changed. But now you feel tired. Perhaps if you give it your very best effort you will crest the top of the hill and enter a plateau of peace and enjoy spiritual victory. You run full speed on your pathway and quickly become exhausted. You are completely spent and disillusioned. You get off the pathway but this time you don't get back on. You walk away, never to return. That pathway to God was actually a treadmill going nowhere.

Many seemingly strong Christians have left their *path* and never returned to Church. Could this have been their experience?

QUESTIONS

1. How was conformity expressed in your group?

2. Were you on a performance treadmill? Describe it.

LEGALISTS ARE JUDGMENTAL

A legalist will think about you according to his rigid assumptions. He interprets what he sees and assigns motive and cause. You might hear him say, "He saw that movie? He must not be very committed to God." Legalists have very long lists of things they approve and disapprove.

When legalists pass judgment, they can be very harsh. In John 9:34 a man born blind was excommunicated because he told the truth about his healing by Jesus. The truth was no defense for him. Legalists find it hard to be merciful. Mercy arises out of love; the spirit of the law competes with the letter of the law. Showing mercy, in their mind, compromises God's law. To outsiders, or non-legalists, this appears as meanness. Love and legalism are like oil and water; they don't mix.

QUESTIONS

1. How was judgmentalism expressed in your group?

2. Were you judged? For what?

LEGALISTS ARE HYPOCRITICAL

Though legalists may preach that salvation is by grace, they imply that you can't be a true Christian if your works don't rise to the level they approve. Some groups teach that certain works are necessary to be saved. They are the modern Judaizers whom Paul anathematized in Galatians 1. They claim Christ is the savior, but His work of salvation must be completed by certain works you perform. Paul asked them in Galatians 3:3, "*Are you so foolish? Having begun by the Spirit, are you now being perfected by the flesh?*" It is hypocritical to claim Christ *and* add your works to His finished work on Calvary.

Every human will fail to live up to any set of laws and ordinances including legalists. However, it seems that they recognize the problem and provide themselves a pressure release valve. One group allows alcohol. Another winks at overly rough play on the ball field that violates the rules of the game and Christian decency. Such outlets let off steam built up by trying to be perfect the rest of the time.

QUESTIONS

1. How was hypocrisy expressed in your group?

2. How did it affect you?

Do an inventory of what makes you vulnerable to legalism including your doctrinal beliefs, personal boundaries, commitment levels to people and organizations. In each of these things you need to find out what is true and hold on to it. Evaluate how you have or have not set or maintained your personal boundaries. Some things are not the business of others without your invitation or permission. A Christian spiritual abuse support group could be exactly what you need to resolve these issues.

QUESTION

1. What issues come to your mind that you might include in your "inventory?" List them:

-
-
-
-
-

2. Do you need someone, or a group, to assist you?

My Personal Journal

"And in vain they worship Me, teaching as doctrines the commandments of men."

Matthew 15:9b

6

Mind Control

"If I were asked today to formulate as concisely as possible that main cause of the ruinous revolution that swallowed up some 60 million of our people, I could not put it more accurately than to repeat: 'Men had forgotten God; that is why all this has happened."

Alexander Solzhenitsyn

At the end of the Korean War, Dr. Robert J. Lifton studied the returned American POWs. Many had succumbed to the Communist brainwashing during their captivity, denounced America and spoke well of their captors and the "workers paradise" of communism. But soon after their return to an American cultural milieu they reverted to their American cultural values. The question in Dr. Lifton's study was why and how red-blooded American boys changed so dramatically and quickly under the communist brainwashing? In his book ***Thought Reform and the Psychology of Totalism*** he outlined eight criteria that can be employed in brainwashing or mind control.

The parallels between the totalitarian methods in the religious and political arenas are remarkable. The difference is in the degree of control and the degree to which dissent is punished. If you have experienced spiritual abuse as part of a system, you will see the connection immediately.

Students of the cults have found that the mind control techniques are being used by most cults in the recruitment and retention of converts. The dark side of human nature is at work finding the most effective methods of control, and these methods also protect those in power from accountability for truth and justice.

Control of others is alien to Christian teaching and to human nature as God originally created us. It is not alien to our fallen nature. However, control can only be exercised in an atmosphere of ignorance, dependence and untruth. Once the light of truth enters, controllers are threatened. The highest goal of the communist dictator or religious cult leader is that his followers remain uninformed and dependent. The ideal state sought by controllers is a childlike dependency. Cults use a subtle version of the techniques used in communist prison camps.

People ask how someone can commit suicide or murder in the name of God, any god. The answer lies in the information they have and the milieu, or environment in which that information is couched. With complete control of information and a person's environment an individual can be programmed to commit radical acts.

There is a difference between brainwashing and mind control. Brainwashing is coercive and violent as our soldiers experienced in their POW camps. Victims are aware that an enemy is trying to change them. He is not their helpful friend. Religious mind control takes place in a much more subtle setting. The guards are replaced by teachers, and people who are there are seemingly helpful. With religious mind control, the controllers simply convince you there is something greater than yourself to which you give your devotion. Then they give you the tools to control *yourself*. However, those tools are the same whether it is brainwashing or mind control.

EIGHT CRITERIA FOR MIND CONTROL

MILIEU CONTROL

Milieu means the environment in which we live, including all our interactions on a daily basis, the information we take in and the information we give out. It includes the people, places, events, and ideas that pass through our daily life. If these can be controlled, the individual will become isolated from alternative support networks and become vulnerable to influence. The Soviet citizen could only get his news from a Communist Party source because western broadcasts were jammed. This was strong control of information and influence.

An example from religious cults would be the new recruit who distances himself from his friends and family who don't believe as he does so he is not "infected" with their worldly views.

In some settings, the members can be taught to actively avoid the very information that could break their bondage. If a Christian offers a book or tract to a cult member the member will almost always refuse the literature because they have been taught it is spiritual poison. The only way to break that hold is to show them their own literature, which they trust, and demonstrate from it that they have been deceived. Trust in false spiritual authority must be exposed for what it is. When that trust is broken, the cult member becomes open to alternative views and the truth can be received.

QUESTION

- Did something "open your eyes" to a deception? Describe what happened.

MYSTICAL MANIPULATION

In any cultic group or authoritarian government there is a higher calling, a utopian goal for which the group strives. The follower accepts that his group is the only one equipped to achieve this goal and their leaders have advanced far beyond them hence they are worthy to be followed. This mystical ideal can be achieved if he will give his all in its pursuit. If he fails to do so the group will fall short of its goal. This is a powerful incentive for religious cults. It is as if God were directing their actions and punishing their shortcomings.

An example in communist history is the Chinese Cultural Revolution with the sayings of Mao in *The Little Red Book*. Another is the Cambodian experience under Pol Pot where everyone was forced into agrarian work, a communist ideological ideal, according to the Khmer Rouge. The capital city, Phnom Penh became a ghost town.

Lifton makes the point that such manipulation requires a level of trust that is difficult, if not impossible, to maintain over a sustained period of time. When trust is lost followers see through the manipulation and cease to respond.

Among the cults a demonstrated false prophecy or the clear proof of a lie can put an end to the leader's ability to manipulate followers on to greater effort.

Manipulation is completely out of place for the Christian. Sometimes admonition and exhortation are replaced with manipulation. Where this happens, it should be resisted.

QUESTIONS

1. What was the goal in your group that required your 100% commitment?

2. How was this used to manipulate you?

THE DEMAND FOR PURITY

The utopian goal can only be achieved by purity of devotion. In the political arena the goal can be achieved by actions consistent with ideological purity. In the religious arena ideology is called doctrine and impurity is called sin. To achieve the utopian goal anything impure must be removed. The leaders get to decide what that purity is in totalistic systems. The followers strive mightily until they fail. Then their failure is written off as an example of the impurity that held the group back from achieving its goal.

In totalistic systems the leaders exhort the followers to search themselves for anything impure that would hold the group back and defeat them. This causes the followers a lot of self-doubt leading to a rigid adherence to the rules of the system.

As Christians we know that the Ten Commandments are pure and true, but man is unable to obey them completely. Our "purity" is Christ's purity imputed to us through faith in His shed blood.

QUESTION

- Were there examples in your experience where failure was attributed to impurity?

THE CULT OF CONFESSION

Closely related to the Demand for Purity is confession. Failure to succeed means confessions must be made. Any weakness or failure, real or perceived, is to be confessed for the sake of the group. This is not legitimate confession to God, or someone wronged, but improper confessions.

Any personal weakness, bad thought, failure to give 100% to the group, must be confessed. Even wrongs not actually committed can be confessed as an example to help the group achieve purity. Our innate sense of guilt because of original sin makes people vulnerable to this.

Confession can have a cathartic effect on the person confessing. It can also provide leverage for the group to use on the person in the future, as often happens in cultic systems. Open confession sessions can create a sense of personal uncertainty. If a seemingly strong person confesses, the weaker followers will feel less sure of their own purity. Inappropriate public confessions erode the boundaries we need to maintain our individuality.

In the communist world, especially China, when a political dissident is tried and found guilty, he will frequently make a public confession of his "guilt." This justifies the political system that will then kill him to purify the "workers paradise".

Christians should only confess actual wrongdoing to God and to the person they wronged. This helps to prevent the erosion of legitimate boundaries of privacy and confidentiality. High control groups benefit by the erosion of these boundaries because it gives the leaders ammunition to support their control.

QUESTION

1. Did you observe, or take part in such confessions in your group?

2. What were your emotions in these sessions?

SACRED SCIENCE

Lifton said, "The totalist milieu maintains an aura of sacredness around its basic dogma, holding it out as the ultimate moral vision for the ordering of human existence."[4] To question it is to blaspheme; questioning must not be allowed in such a system. Questions imply an issue is unsettled, and therefore uncertain. Questioning spreads to others and undermines the hold of the leadership.

In the Soviet Union the Communist Party was the ideological master. In every military unit there was a "*zampolit*", or political officer, who kept everyone in line with the Party ideology. When Gorbachev instituted "*glasnost*" (openness) outside sources of information could be accessed. The sacred science of the Party line could be questioned. The people were empowered by new information and, as a result, the communist system had to go. This is what every cult leader fears most. (One cult calls it "independent thinking" and condemns it as an "evidence of pride.")

For a Christian questioning is not a sin. It is not even doubt, but unbelief, that is sin. The examples are many from Genesis to Revelation that God wants a two-way relationship with us (Job 9, 10 and 38). He is big enough to handle our questions.

QUESTIONS

1. Were you criticized for questioning? What happened?

4 Robert J. Lifton, *Thought Reform and Psychology of Totalism*, The University of North Carolina Press, page 427

2. How did it affect you?

3. Did you observe someone else being criticized? Describe

4. Did it cause you to want to question or to avoid future criticism?

LOADING THE LANGUAGE

Lifton said, "The language of the totalist environment is characterized by the thought-terminating cliché."[5]

Certain words and phrases are so loaded with meaning that stark choices are implied leading to the end of critical thinking. In a cult setting an example is the phrase "*theocratic arrangement.*" This term is meant to imply to the members that God has appointed the organization as His channel of communication to mankind and has invested it with a level of authority and truth equivalent to that of an Old Testament prophet. If a member questions his organization, it can be stopped by saying that it is God's theocratic arrangement. The implication for the questioner is that he is disagreeing with God. Within such totalistic systems the alternatives are usually stark black and white choices.

For example, the communists used the term 'bourgeois mentality' to categorize any thoughts or behavior they disapproved. Since disapproval could easily lead to censure, the use of the term was a shorthand warning to anyone not obeying the party line.

5 Ibid, page 429

For the Christian a thought stopping cliché is the same as manipulation. It is opposed to the principle of accountability and the reality that truth can stand the test.

QUESTION

- Can you think of phrases that were used to stifle discussion? Make a list of them.

DOCTRINE OVER PERSON

What you see, hear or think is irrelevant in the face of the group's doctrine. You must submerge your opinions in the group's worldview. If a person's experience is contrary to the group's doctrine, then the doctrine must win out and personal experience must be dismissed. If the doctrine does not square with reality and questioning and disagreement is prohibited, the ultimate end of such a system is total collapse. It is not possible, short of revolution, to rescue the system.

The classic example of this is the socialist command economy of the old Soviet Union. The doctrine held that the people, as represented by the State, owned all property. They expressed this communal system with the adage—"From each according to his means, to each according to his need." The fallacy of this system is that productivity never rose to what was commanded because the model failed to account for a fundamental truth - the self-interested motivation of the citizen. When the product of your labor is taken from you to be given to others, the motivation to produce goes with it. When you can keep the product of your labor, you are motivated to produce. The end of the Soviet experiment was economic collapse and the replacement of much of the system with a barter economy, and capitalism.

The Christian holds that doctrine is consistent with reality, and therefore consistent with personal experience, because both are derived from God. Where tensions appear between doctrines and experience the Christian must seek more knowledge and wisdom. Questioning inherited assumptions is a healthy exercise. Given time such tensions will disappear (as was the case with Galileo's position that the Earth revolved around the Sun while the Catholic Church said the opposite.)

QUESTION

- Did you observe, or experience a situation, where the group devalued the individual because they questioned the group? What happened?

THE DISPENSING OF EXISTENCE

The system of doctrine is so sacred that only those who adhere to it are "real" people. Those outside the system (or those who question) are expendable. When questions are raised there will be an application of control mechanisms as described earlier. If that does not stop the questioning, the person can be "eliminated."

Elimination takes different forms with different groups. For the communists it meant the Gulag, a re-education camp, or death. In a cult, it often means disfellowshipping, to completely ostracize the offender from other cult members and so keep the group pure.

In legalistic Christian groups the rule can become more important than the individual. The person at odds with the group is labeled as a rebel, troublemaker, or divisive. It is then easier to dismiss the person.

The Pharisees attempted to silence or discredit Jesus (and later the Apostles.) Later in church history many have paid the ultimate price for violating the sense of order and truth as set forth by those in power.

QUESTIONS

1. Did the group "dispense" with people who crossed the line of what was acceptable?

2. What form did it take?

My Personal Journal

"Beware of the false prophets, who come to you in sheep's clothing, but inwardly are ravenous wolves. You will know them by their fruits. Grapes are not gathered from thorn bushes nor figs from thistles, are they?"

Matthew 7:15-16

7

The Stages of Involvement and Exit

People who spend time in a legalistic or high control group typically follow a process as they assimilate the teachings and social dynamics of the group. The group also will use subtle, and not-so-subtle, methods to recruit, indoctrinate, and keep its members. In this chapter we will look at these processes from the beginning of entrapment in the system to final freedom from it. There are five clear stages.

Stage One: Recruitment or Enlistment

If someone is raised in an abusive system, they may never consciously choose whether to stay or leave. For others there is usually a time when he or she makes a decision to join a group.

Recruiting methods include exploitation of a personal crisis, or a focus on problems in the world to which only the group seems to have the solution. They may seem to have an answer to every question, demonstrating how superior they are to every other alternative group. They often offer immediate friendship without the usual cultivation of a relationship. They may also create confusion or cause questioning as a preliminary step to providing the solutions that will make them appear to be what they say about themselves. In all these methods, outright deception is frequently employed.

Recruitment

Exploitation of a personal crisis

Answers

Superiority

Friendship

Confusion

Deception

At this stage the group seems ideal to the potential recruit. It has a lot of positives and few, if any, negatives. The recruit adopts the basic culture of the group. This includes an elitist attitude, and an "us vs. them" view of outside groups. Association with non-member outsiders is usually restricted as well, especially for teenage children.

The indoctrination can begin even before one has formally become a part of the group. This usually involves large amounts of time spent in study. After the basic teachings of the group are learned, the recruit may be put to work in some way that reduces time for reflective thought, uses up available time for any old relationships (especially family) and has the effect of reinforcing the group ideology. One of the most common indoctrination tools is the use of fear and guilt to minimize questioning, dull critical thinking skills, and create a childlike trust and dependency on the group or its leaders. A system of rewards and punishment keeps the recruit on the prescribed path of dependency on the leaders.

Along the way tough choices are required as the recruit begins to notice some of the negatives he missed at the beginning. However, the alternative at this point is rejection of the whole group or system, so problems are rationalized away in comparison to the larger good. This can lead to a searing of the conscience and long-term bondage to a dysfunctional system, or it can lead to the Second stage....

Stage Two: Dissonance

Some who hear their conscience telling them something is not right will interpret it as doubt or a spiritual attack by demons. These thought-stopping reactions are part of the indoctrination by the group. They don't want anyone thinking for himself. To refuse to listen to the voice inside that warns of danger will sear the conscience and reduce future sensitivity to the truth or the work of God's Spirit.

If the recruit still hears that voice telling him something is not right, then he may begin his exit at this stage. He may not realize his exit has begun but the process is at work. It will help in the exit process to understand how the process works to break one away from the grip of a strong conviction. This process works both ways, for good and bad, to draw you into the group and to pull you out of it.

Here is where we find the answer to how people get snared in high control groups, and how personalities are dramatically changed for the worse.

There is a process behind a dramatic and destructive personality change where a person will accept something that would not otherwise be believable. It is called *cognitive dissonance theory*. Leon Festinger, author of *When Prophecy Fails* described three elements of social psychology and behavior modification techniques at work in a cult environment, or milieu. They are Behavior, Thought, and Emotions. Steven Hassan, ex-Moonie, and author of *Combating Cult Mind Control,* added Information to the list and called it the BITE model for Behavior, Information, Thought, and Emotion.

BITE

Behavior
Information
Thought
Emotions

Festinger said that if you can control behavior, emotions, and thought, you could get a group of people to do very bizarre and wrong things. If one of the three elements is changed the others will be powerfully influenced to come into agreement with it, perhaps because people don't like being hypocritical.

When someone is recruited into a mind-controlling cult, his or her behavior and personality begin to change dramatically. Someone who has known this person for years will be struck with the significance of the change and comment, "He's just not the person I used to know. What happened?"

New recruits to totalistic groups experience "thought reform" as the starting point in behavior modification. It begins with acceptance of a totally new worldview premise underlying the cult. This premise could be Hassan's Information. The worldview may be that all of current Christianity is apostate and in need of a restoration. It may be that God only speaks to and through a particular chosen leader and you must listen to him to hear God. It may be the "special" or "spiritual elite" status of the group. This foundation must be laid for the acceptance of the teachings and practices espoused by the group. If the recruit has accepted the premise, then secondary teachings and lifestyle practices must be followed or he will be in a continual state of cognitive dissonance, mental conflict, or hypocrisy. He will neither be "in" nor "out" of the group but in a limbo condition the group will frown on, leaving the person to feel he is spiritually weak or second-class. This drives the recruit to try to resolve the problems and become one of the "in" people.

There is a less thorough manifestation of these control mechanisms in legalistic groups. Such groups let their people live their individual lives, but use fear, guilt, idealism, and legalistic rules to put them on a religious treadmill. The legalistic Christian will frequently feel guilty, inadequate, a failure, and worn out after years of such rule keeping.

The antidote is truth, unimpeachably presented. When a person caught up in a system sees the truth, the same cognitive dissonance by which he was recruited begins to set him free. It is the BITE elements at work again. He doesn't want to by a hypocrite after all. At this point the Third Stage begins....

Stage Three: Rebellion

The system will notice a member's uneasiness, absence from events, questions, and more. All these outwardly observable evidences will tell the suspicious and paranoid group that he is "in rebellion" against God. He is in rebellion, but not against God; He is rebelling against a false version of Christianity that enslaves and violates conscience and grieves God.

During this stage the rebelling member will hear warnings about talking to people outside the group or reading information contrary to the group doctrine. When the group or its leaders notice the member is not as committed as before he may begin hearing them talk about demonic influence or getting back to full-fledged commitment to the group as a way to dispel doubts. Experiencing doubts while still in the group makes leaving sound attractive. Should he leave, however, he may well experience a period of self-doubt where he worries, he may have turned his back on God.

If you are at this stage, remember that fear is not of God (Romans 8:15 and 2 Timothy 1:7). He has given us a sound mind to use in thinking through the issues. With your Bible in hand, a prayer for God's leading on your lips, and the promise that God's Spirit will lead us into all truth, take courage and begin your search for answers. Do not sear your conscience. Truth will set you free. This brings you to the Fourth Stage....

Stage Four: Counting the Cost

At this stage the member begins to think about leaving. That thought brings to mind some scary alternatives. First, the idea that the group is what it claims to be, has not been completely forsaken. And, to leave would be like turning your back on God's will for you. Most high control groups will regularly tell their people that leaving the group opens them up to Satan's attacks, and they will be out from under God's protective covering and will get cancer or other serious ailments, and experience personal disasters. None of this is true of the way God deals with us. Don't believe it.

If your life is wrapped up in the group, you will lose your friends, perhaps your job; you may have to change who handles your business affairs; you may even lose your family if they are part of the group.

Long-term exposure to a high level of control leads to dependency on the group. Separation can be very traumatic. Involvement can also cause emotional and mental disorders for which a professional counselor should be consulted. If you have spent years in a high control religion do not hesitate to seek out professional help. Don't assume that you are objective enough to evaluate yourself. An experienced and objective counselor may do that for you.

Despite the serious consequences that may be inherent in leaving a spiritually abusive group, don't delay. You have time on your side as you consider the Fifth Stage ...

Stage Five: The Exit

One of the important facets of ministries to cults and high control groups is exit counseling. These ministries help people transition from high control groups with false doctrines to a grace-oriented Christian walk founded on genuine New Testament teaching.

One effect of leaving a high control group is a sense of emotional decompression. The pressures of the system are removed and that is a great thing. However, other pressures immediately take over. Questions arise; "Did I do the right thing? What does God think of me now? Should I go back? At least I had friends in the group!"

Many who leave a high control group do go back—at least for a time. The outside is too scary, or they are not yet fully convinced of the error of the group. However, as they re-enter the group, their conscience begins to bother them again. It's not the same as when they first joined.

Stages of Involvement

Recruitment
Dissonance
Rebellion
Counting the Cost
The Exit

When the Israelites fled Egypt with Moses, many of them wanted to return. The problems they knew in Egypt were better than the unknown future. If you have fled from your Egypt, remember the Promised Land of freedom in Christ is ahead of you. You are not the first to be in your position, and you will certainly not be the last.

You are venturing into the unknown. You are searching for truth. You'll need to make new friends, though that can be difficult initially because you don't know whom you can trust. You may be searching for a new church, and that is perhaps the most difficult step—You don't want to step into another abuse situation. Mark Twain said, "We should be careful to get out of an experience only the wisdom that is in it—and stop there; lest we be like the cat that sits down on a hot stove-lid. She will never sit down on a hot stove—lid again—and that is well; but she will also never sit down on a cold one anymore."[6] Being burned once is enough to keep you away from organized religion for a long, long time. In fact, many who have been abused never return to church. For the moment, don't rush into seeking a new church home. Give yourself time to heal.

While this stage can be frightening, it can also be exciting. God does not require endless performance from you in order to love you. Learning this can free you from a powerful bondage. God wants to meet you where you are and help you be in His will. When you grasp this, it can do wonders for how you view God. God does not stand off from us and say, "Where you are is far from me. You must become better before I will love you." He comes to us where we are and daily teaches us how we can learn to love Him. Then from our love will flow a positive response to God's will for us.

Set limits for yourself as you re-examine your belief system. ... Those limits should include the basics of Christianity.

Obligation creates heavy loads. Love lifts those burdens. This realization is wonderfully liberating. Biblical Christi-

6 Mark Twain, *Following the Equator*, Pudd'nhead Wilson's New Calendar

anity is a positive, onward- and upward-looking attitude, rather than a preoccupation with all the unacceptable baggage we carry as sinners. We focus not on our sins but on the One who saves us from them.

Set limits for yourself as you re-examine your belief system. Some have thrown out the baby (belief in God) with the bathwater (a spiritually abusive group) in their rejection of their past experience. Determine that you won't do this to yourself. That limit should include the basics of Christianity. Find a mature Christian who will listen compassionately and confidentially as you purge past poisons from your system. If you do not have someone locally, contact me.

QUESTIONS

1. What attracted you to the group in the first place?

2. What are, or were, the issues that caused dissonance?

3. What did the group do when your unease became apparent (if you are past that stage)?

4. In thinking about leaving what questions or struggles came to mind?

5. How do you feel about your future out of the group?

Obligation creates heavy loads. Love lifts those burdens.

6. Are you able to see the group as the "Egypt" of your own Exodus?

My Personal Journal

"And you shall know the truth, and the truth shall make you free."

John 8:32

8

Responsibility and Recovery

"If I can put one touch of rosy sunset into the life of any man or woman, I shall feel that I have worked with God."
G.K. Chesterton

WHO IS RESPONSIBLE?

There are two questions that may be emotionally difficult to consider, but nevertheless need to be thought out for the sake of your future spiritual decisions.

1. When spiritual abuse happens, who is responsible?
2. How does a Christian guard against it?

If you have experienced and internalized the high control and manipulative tactics of an abusive group, then you are a "victim" of spiritual abuse. If you did not internalize it then you are not a victim. (Abuse happened but you did not allow yourself to be hurt by it.) This is an important principle in understanding the phenomenon of abuse.

The abuser has his responsibility before God and man, and his responsibility is greater than yours because of his leadership role. But, we also have our own responsibility for choices that put us in the position of being abused. We must be discerning. We make choices and we must accept the consequences of those choices.

> *Key elements missing where abuse happens:*
>
> - Sufficient knowledge
> - Critical thinking skills necessary for discernment

The key elements missing where abuse happens are sufficient knowledge and critical thinking skills necessary for discernment. To discern is to compare a known truth with a claim of truth and come to a fair judgment. We do that every day in many other fields. However, in our Christian walk we start out as new believers with a significant lack of knowledge. This is to be expected. Later in our Christian walk we can still misunderstand the Bible if a trusted leader tells us something untrue.

Jesus was "spiritually abused" by the religious leaders (Pharisees, Sadducees, Sanhedrin) but, of course, He never internalized it and therefore was always above the problem. Being omniscient He knew exactly what was happening and confronted their false spiritual leadership by calling them whitewashed sepulchers, hypocrites, etc. (Matthew 23). This didn't endear Jesus to those who thought they had power. They sought even more to do away with this troublesome Rabbi. They had no idea the Power they were dealing with because they had seared their consciences and were blind to the scriptures.

We don't have His omniscience. Many abuse victims are like newborn babies in their knowledge and discernment. Some are further handicapped in acquiring needed knowledge when the group that brought them to Christ is also a troubled and dysfunctional body. That is very much like a baby born into a dysfunctional family. The baby can be scarred for a lifetime by the dysfunctions of his family. With knowledge, experience, and maturity though, a child can overcome its disadvantages, just as Christians from a dysfunctional spiritual experience can overcome their background if they will choose to develop their discernment skills. Most discover this truth too late, and they must deal with spiritual and emotional damage.

Five Elements are needed to develop discernment to help find balance in an often-troubled spiritual scene.

- **The Bible**—Truth
- **The Holy Spirit**—Who will guide us into all truth.
- **A teachable attitude**—a learner and seeker of knowledge.
- **Critical thinking**—to compare and judge facts.
- **Awareness of a diversity of views**—not dependent on only one human source.

The second gem of the six gems of wisdom contained in Randall Arthur's book ***Wisdom Hunter*** addresses this problem of discernment. He wrote, "*I will honestly question everything first. Likewise, if I ever, in any situation, try to share my beliefs with others, I will neither ask nor expect them to blindly believe me. I will encourage them to honestly question and challenge everything I say. One who learns through the process of honest questioning, objective thinking, and respectful challenging is more apt to know in the end what is really true. And he will also know 'why' he believes it.*"[7]

A summary of Randall Arthur's second gem of wisdom is that believers will throughout their life face either honest questioning or blind believing:

- **Honest questioning is always good because truth will always stand the test** (Acts 17:10-11).
- **Questioning teaches us how to think critically.**
- **Blind believing leads to Pharisaism and bondage to human traditions.**[8]

7 Randall Arthur, *Wisdom Hunter*, Multnomah, pages 133-134

8 Ibid, pages 131-134

If you are reading this, you are probably on the exit side of an abusive experience. You may be somewhat better equipped now with the elements described above than before your abuse. If that is the case, then you gained them the hard way.

You no doubt experienced disillusionment. There is a silver lining if you are willing to look for it. Break the word disillusionment down to its component parts: "*Dis*" means to remove or take away. "*Illusion*" is something that is not real or true. To have an illusion taken away is good.

You must replace illusion with reality, even while you feel worse than you have ever felt, and with great uncertainty about spiritual things. The Good Shepherd has left the ninety-nine safe sheep and is looking for you. There are Christians who know how to help you.

QUESTIONS

1. What was your responsibility in your abuse?

2. How can you resolve that, learn from it, and move on?

You must replace illusion with reality ... The Good Shepherd has left the ninety-nine safe sheep and is looking for you.

3. How do you feel about the responsibility of the person or group that committed the abuse in light of what you learned in this chapter?

RECOVERY

"In the struggle for existence, it is only on those who hang on for ten minutes after all is hopeless, that hope begins to dawn."
G.K. Chesterton

The final part of our discussion deals with recovery, which begins with your decision to reject the group as your spiritual home.

Earlier in this workbook we reviewed the five stages from the beginning of your entry into the high control system to your final exit. The last two of those stages are vital in recovery.

COUNTING THE COST

When you have decided to leave a high control group you will feel a wide range of emotions that may include confusion, fear, hope, guilt, anxiety, anger, and excitement—sometimes in rapid succession. While you are in the middle of this emotional roller coaster you will wonder if it will ever end. Yes, it will. Your emotional responses to spiritual abuse are normal.

Your decision to leave is a life-changing and important step you are taking and there will be costs associated with it. You can help yourself tremendously if you will do a few important things during the last two stages (*Counting the Cost* and *Exit*) of the five stages of your involvement with the high control group.

Expect to lose friends. There is no way around this reality. Those "friends" may also say some bad things about you. Don't be surprised. They are captives of a system that has shaped their thinking and the way they respond. You may also find that family becomes estranged from you if they are part of the group. Hopefully this will not happen but be prepared for it.

Your decision to leave is a life-changing and important step you are taking and there will be costs associated with it.

One couple, that I helped out of a high control group said they had to start all over again with a new faith, new friends and even a new insurance agent. They had, as much as possible, limited their environment to those people in the group. They left it all behind.

Of the costs to consider, is the fear and guilt you may feel after leaving. It is actually quite common for someone who leaves to return after a short while on the outside. They feel insecure or fearful that they have turned their back on God. When they return to the group, however, they feel the emotional conflict again that originally caused them to leave.

Anyone going through a traumatic exit needs a friend, a counselor, someone who can listen with understanding and offer gracious support as they ride an emotional roller coaster with you, while working through the stages of recovery. Someone who has already been through an experience of spiritual abuse and found healing is the best possible person to help you. Whether you find such a friend or not, you can help yourself with books and Internet websites that address the issues. There is a recommended reading list at the end of this workbook. Also feel free to contact me. My contact information is at the end of this book under "Need Help?"

You need to examine two areas that may have been factors to your entry in the first place. One is your family of origin. Was your childhood marked by conditional love? Were you verbally abused? Was there an environment that fostered undue submission and dependence on authorities? Did you have a shame-based identity? If your family background predisposed you to be attracted to a high-control group, counseling can help you deal with the damage and keep you from repeating the error.

The second area is the doctrinal beliefs of the group. Were certain doctrines taught that caused you to think they were special, unique, elite, or God-ordained? You need to submit those teachings to the test of scripture. If your experience was abusive and controlling, that by itself should tell you the group and/or its leaders were acting contrary to the way Jesus would have them lead. The doctrines they used to keep you in submission to them are certainly contrary to scripture.

If you need someone to talk to about your struggle, I am available. I understand the emotional conflicts and I have experience in helping spiritual abuse victims to resolve them. I can also put you in touch with others who have left groups like yours and who have willing ears and empathetic hearts. There is no reason you should go through this alone.

QUESTIONS

1. What "costs" do you face in leaving the group?

2. Do you have the support of family or friends as you leave?

3. Are you able to plan for your future, such as finding a new place to live, a way to support yourself or, eventually a place for Christian fellowship?

THE EXIT

The final stage is your actual Exit. The issues you will most likely face include:

- Sorting out your emotional responses to the things that trigger your memories.
- Sorting out your beliefs
- Struggling with your ability to trust again.
- The need to find a new group that will meet your need for a sense of community and belonging.
- The need to restore (or find for the first time) a healthy relationship with God.

In the midst of these issues, you will wonder if your struggle will ever end. It will, but it will take time and will call for you to be patient with yourself and others. Give yourself all the time you need. God certainly will. He is patient and knows the beginning of your struggle from the end of it.

If you give yourself time and get the help you need, you can come out healthier and stronger than if you had never experienced spiritual abuse. You will be able to look back in retrospect and see God's hand as He taught, guided and protected you.

QUESTIONS

1. What stage have you reached in your involvement with your group?

   Recruitment/Enlistment—

   Dissonance—

   Rebellion—

   Counting the Cost—

   Exiting—

2. List some questions or issues where you need help.

3. List specific resources you will consult to get the help you need.

WHAT ABOUT TRIGGERS

A trigger is something that happens after you leave the group that immediately throws you back, mentally, to how you felt or believed in the group, or stirs up your anger at the trauma the experience caused. A pet phrase or a verse from the Bible can trigger such emotions. It can be anything you associate with your abuse experience. Triggers are everywhere, initially.

When you are triggered, you will feel a rush of anger, bitterness, cynicism, fear, disappointment, or regret. This will linger for a long time. It is part of the grieving process, just as if you lost a loved one. However, in the death of a loved one you immediately recognize that the new reality is irreversible. You also know that everyone experiences such losses, they grieve for a period, and then get on with their lives as best they can. With your emotional struggles following the exit from an abusive group you will be triggered repeatedly, potentially for a long time. Taking proper steps to find healing will shorten that time.

You will always feel some sense of loss that you regret. That loss includes the innocence and trust you had at one time. It will also include the lost years you spent in the group. You may feel a sense of embarrassment at having been fooled into joining a group that you now see as abnormal. That is frequently how ex-cultists feel. From the perspective of four decades dealing with cults and other high control religions almost all Christians are intrigued by the story of someone's deliverance from deception. You need not feel embarrassed. Remember, we are all ignorant about different things. After successfully working through these struggles, you will probably be wiser than most.

QUESTIONS

1. What triggers you?

2. How do you deal with these emotions?

3. Have you found a compassionate listener to help you? Explain.

FINDING COMMUNITY

"One sees great things from the valley; only small things from the peak."
G.K. Chesterton

Everyone needs a sense of community. One attraction of your group was probably that it provided social support and acceptance. When you are wounded by so-called "friendly fire" coming from your own spiritual community you will face a lot of triggers when you are among people of faith who use some of the same terms or concepts. This can cause you to avoid any Christians. You still need a sense of community where you are encouraged, supported, and can find acceptance just as you are. You can find that community in a variety of places, such as another church, a Bible study group, civic groups, group recreational activities like a sports league, or a host of other groups. Your community might be one or two friends with whom you spend time. If it involves regular physical activity, all the better. It will help you let off steam.

If you move your spiritual involvement to another church look for one that is unlike the one where you experienced abuse. It should be orthodox in its doctrine but not be legalistic. A soccer teammate of mine had a background in an extreme mind control cult. I asked him, "Where are you going now?" He gave me the name of a high liturgy denomination. I asked why he attended there given the stark contrast between the two groups. He said, "Because they don't hassle you."

You need time to rest and sort out your questions and resolve emotionally loaded issues. You need space and a community where you are not "hassled" or triggered by things that remind you of your bad experience.

You want relationships of mutual respect. You need to discern whether your new community accepts you as you are and gives you space while coping with your issues. Such an environment allows you to learn about personal boundaries. An abusive group violates boundaries with the effect that you deny your personhood and individuality. You need to restore, or create those boundaries, for the first time. Some who have been raised in abusive environments never knew they had the right to protect themselves in intimate areas of their soul.

Recognize that you are made in the image of God, and He puts a lot of value in you. You have a stewardship responsibility to God to take good care of His image in you and to guard your soul. That is why grace is so central to the gospel. God wants us to be free so we can choose Him freely. He made us this way. Don't let anyone rob you of your God-given freedom. They are not only robbing you, but they are also robbing God.

QUESTIONS

1. Have you found your "community"? Describe it.

2. Are you willing to find another church community? If not, why not?

3. How are you dealing with triggers?

EVALUATING BELIEFS

"Involuntary ignorance is not charged against you as a fault; but your fault is this—you neglect to inquire into the things you are ignorant of."
Augustine

The stewardship of your soul in theology is called the *priesthood of the believer.* Because of Christ's payment for our sins, we have the right to go directly before the throne of grace, the very presence of God, to talk with Him. One of the hallmarks of an abusive group is that they take away your right to hear directly from God, or to interpret scripture for yourself.

Between you and God is your Advocate, Jesus Christ, who intercedes with the Father on your behalf. Also, the Holy Spirit speaks to you what the Father wants you to hear. In high control systems, the group or its leaders hijack this personal communication with God, and they inform you that when you hear from God it will be through them.

Two-way accountability is quickly discarded in abusive groups in favor of the leader or group being accountable only to God (certainly not to you). If you raise questions they might say, "*Touch not the Lord's anointed.*" You may be told you are out from under your "spiritual covering" or "umbrella of protection" and that you must submit to your "God ordained authority." That authority, they will tell you, will answer to God for himself but you answer to him. This is an unbiblical teaching. It was introduced into Western Christianity through the teachings of Watchman Nee and his book *Spiritual Authority*. Wherever it is taught you will find wounded Christians.

The biblical teaching on two-way accountability is illustrated by Paul's praise of the Bereans who "*searched the scriptures daily*" to see if what they were being told was true. We are to "*put to the test those who call themselves apostles, and they are not*" (Revelation 2:2) The admonition in Jude 3 and 4 to "*contend earnestly for the faith*" is addressed to Christians, who are to examine certain men who have sneaked into the church to teach false doctrines.

Genuine two-way accountability has checks and balances built into the church governmental system. There should be bylaws, financial openness, consultation with, (or voting by) the congregation about church decisions, and a system for bringing a charge against a brother according to Matthew 18. In abusive groups, the last step of Matthew 18 (bringing the brother charged with the offense before the whole congregation) is not allowed. If the offender is a leader there must be a method available to the congregation to fulfill the biblical mandate. When you are searching for a new church home be sure to look for the bylaws. Ask long time members or leaders about problems and how they are handled. A spiritually healthy group is open to questions and keeps an "open book" with respect to its operations.

QUESTIONS

1. How does the priesthood of the believer afford protection against abuse?

2. What are your thoughts on "touching the Lord's anointed?"

LEARNING TO TRUST AGAIN

"You cannot grow a beard in a moment of passion."
G.K. Chesterton

One of the first casualties of an abuse experience is the ability to trust. Gone are the days of confidence that a spiritual leader will do the right thing toward you. Everything any spiritual leader does or says will be doubted first. All leaders must now earn any respect they receive.

You should know two things. First, abusive leaders are the exception, not the rule. Most ministers are truly godly and will lead with a servant's heart. Second, you can learn to seek out that type spiritual leader. If you were going to hire someone to do important structural work on your home, you would ask trusted people who they recommend. You would want to see some of the work they did for someone else. You would ask for references. You can do background checks with spiritual leaders as well.

You will struggle with your distrust, but you must learn to trust again. It is normal for people to extend trust just like a business would extend credit. It is part of daily living. Not extending trust limits you. Learn how to trust; ask questions; hold leaders to account. Exercise a healthy skepticism because it can help you restore your ability to trust again. Extend trust as you are able; it is the best way to regain the ability.

When you consider a new church home talk to the pastor and explain your struggle. Explain that you may need to question him about things that bother you. If he is genuinely a servant leader, he will welcome it. (If he is not then you want to keep looking for a leader who will give you that freedom.)

Spiritual abuse came at the hands of humans who should bear their full guilt, but a victim will often expand that guilt to God. "How could God allow this to happen to me when I was trying to serve Him?" That is a difficult question to answer because we don't have God's perspective, nor do we know what God's purpose is in our experience. The book of Job offers some insight. There was nothing in Job's life to explain why he suddenly got dumped on. He was trying to serve God and we don't read anything about sin in his life that left him exposed to its consequences. His so-called friends had their theories, but they only compounded his problem by blaming him.

Unlike your particular experience the Book of Job does give insight into why Job was put through his trial. There was a debate going on to which Job was not privy. It took place in the spiritual arena between God and Lucifer over whether Job was truly committed to God. God allowed him to be tested. In that test we learn some important lessons about God's love and sovereignty, His sustaining strength and love for us. We also see a wonderful testimony in Job's faith.

We are not guaranteed a safe life or complete protection from evil. The scriptures say that we will not be allowed to be tempted above what we are able to resist through God's strength. When we endure trials two things happen. First, the world is watching as well as other believers. We present a testimony in our afflictions that God can use. Second, our endurance of trials equips us to minister to others who are similarly afflicted, especially unbelievers.

> *"Blessed by the God and Father of our Lord Jesus Christ, the Father of mercies and God of all comfort; who comforts us in all our affliction so that we may be able to comfort those who are in any affliction with the comfort with which we ourselves are comforted by God."*
>
> 2 Corinthians 1:3-4

When you are able to offer help to someone else who has been abused and your experience gives you the insights and wisdom to guide them in the right direction, you will experience a sense of fulfillment and purpose for your own trial.

QUESTIONS

1. Are you able to trust a spiritual leader yet? Why, or why not?

2. How have you resolved the question of why God allowed you to experience abuse?

3. Do you still need help finding answers? Where will you look?

4. Do you have someone to talk to about it? Explain.

5. Have you found a new church home? What did you overcome to do so?

6. Have you talked to the pastor or members about your concerns? How did they respond?

GETTING INTO THE SCRIPTURES

Reading the Bible after spiritual abuse can be a trigger that causes emotional struggles. I know of people who had to overcome emotional obstacles to read the Bible, or certain parts of it. If that is your experience, remember two simple realities.

First, the Bible and its Author, God, are squarely on the side of the spiritual abuse victim. There are numerous passages in the Bible where God says some harsh things to the abusers of His people. And God's heart is to pursue you and help you find peace and healing.

In the story of the lost sheep, the Good Shepherd leaves the 99 who are safe to find the one that was lost. God will come looking for you to bind up your wounds and He will give you the time you need to recover. He will not place urgent "to do" lists in front of you.

Second, the abuse you experienced came from human hands, not from God. Abusive leaders may try to reinforce their authority with "God talk" that puts followers in the difficult position of seeming to question God or the Bible. It is not true. Godly leaders recognize the difference between rebellion and the need to understand.

If reading the Bible triggers you begin by studying the Gospel of Matthew, the Psalms and Proverbs. These books are positive and encouraging and address the inner conflicts of a spiritual struggle. If you need to, begin with short passages and work up from there. In time you will be able to read more of the Bible without being triggered.

QUESTIONS

1. Are you able to read or study the Bible without emotional conflicts? What do you do when conflict arises in you when reading?

2. Do you see yourself as a "lost sheep" whom the Good Shepherd is seeking? Explain.

3. Do you feel God is judging you? Explain.

TRUSTING GOD

"Let your religion be less of a theory and more of a love affair."
G.K. Chesterton

There is also the question of God's role in your experience. God is not punishing you. In fact, the opposite is true. The sin of spiritual abuse against you was also a sin against Him because you bear His image. This makes Him angry, but not with you.

Jesus' response to spiritual abusers is displayed in His response to the moneychangers in the Temple. They were cheating God's people to make more money than was proper. They were using God's people and taking advantage of their spiritual sincerity to serve their own corrupt purposes. Jesus displayed violent righteous anger, but not toward the people—toward their abusers.

Today spiritually abusive leaders still use God's house as the setting to meet their own needs at the expense of followers who are sincere in their desire to serve God. They will pay the penalty eventually. A review of Chapter One: True vs. False Christian Leadership will help you each time you struggle with trusting God or spiritual leaders.

QUESTION

1. Can you accept the idea that God allowed your experience for some larger purpose, like that of Job? Explain

2. You may have had some role in getting into a spiritually abusive situation. What caused you to be vulnerable to recruitment?

WHAT ABOUT FORGIVENESS

"The Bible tells us to love our neighbors, and also to love our enemies; probably because they are generally the same people."
G.K. Chesterton

If asked, have you forgiven the person who abused you what would you say? Forgiveness is the most difficult part of recovery, and it should not be considered lightly. It is possible, though not helpful, to go through the motions of forgiveness and later find that you had not fully forgiven. Your healing process will eventually require full forgiveness of the abuser. Jesus said of those who crucified Him, "*Father, forgive them; for they do not know what they are doing.*" Ask Him for the resources you need to experience the gift of forgiveness, as well.

The reality in this situation is that an abusive leader either does not know he is abusive, or does, and denies his guilt. Recognize how insecure and weak these people are. They are compensating for their weak faith or personal needs by using and abusing people. If you tell them face to face that you forgive them, they may scoff or brush it off. That is their problem. However, not forgiving will remain your problem until you are able to do it. Forgiving is more about *you* than it is about your abuser. You do it because you need to, not because they need it from you.

Forgiving does not equate to respect, which is earned by doing what is right. Leaders who deny their guilt and continue to be abusive do not deserve respect. Not respecting them as a spiritual leader is not a sin; it is recognizing reality. It was in the final stages of Jesus relationship with the Pharisees, after they had seen His miracles, heard His sermons, and He had spoken the truth about their hypocrisy, yet they still refused to acknowledge He was the Son of God. It was at this point that He called them what they were, hypocrites, whitewashed sepulchers, and a brood of vipers. It was not sin. It was true. Jesus did not respect them.

Some will say we should "*touch not the Lord's anointed*" as a way to shut off criticism of a spiritual leader. Psalms 105:15 says, "*Touch not mine anointed, and do my prophets no harm.*" According to *Clarke's Commentary* those who were the "anointed" in this passage were probably the patriarchs. He also says "prophets, priests, and kings were always anointed."[9] The act of anointing a priest or king in this time was like a badge of office. It was not something any person claimed independently. Prophets demonstrated their anointing by the power of God backing up their words. In 1st Samuel 24:6 God tells David to "touch not the Lord's anointed," meaning King Saul. To "touch" in that context meant physical harm and not criticism. David did criticize Saul in 1st Samuel 24:12. Therefore, "touch not" does not mean criticism. It means physical harm.

In Deuteronomy chapters 13 and 18 those who claimed to speak for God were to be put to a stern test. If they failed the test the people of Israel were authorized by God to exact a severe penalty. The same test, but a less severe penalty, exists in the New Testament. How do you discern the difference between those claiming to speak for God and those who are truly godly? Ultimately, every believer must discern and decide based upon the scripture and the evidence in the life of the leader. When a Christian leader is

9 Adam Clarke, *A Commentary and Critical Notes*, Abingdon, page 554

truly godly in his service, he should be given all the support and encouragement possible. When a leader leads badly, he should be accountable to those whom he leads. If he refuses correction, separate yourself from him and let God deal with his error.

QUESTIONS

1. Are you able to forgive your abuser? Explain.

2. Have you asked God to equip you emotionally and spiritually to be able to forgive? What has been the result?

3. What is your level of respect for your abuser? Explain.

HELPING OTHERS TOWARD RECOVERY

"Courage is not simply one of the virtues but the form of every virtue at the testing point."
C.S. Lewis

The sign that you have turned the corner in your recovery is when you can help someone else find hope for their own recovery. It is at this point that your difficult experience acquires meaning and purpose. You can find opportunity to help others in a support group, or through personal conversation. You are probably not the only person who has left your particular abusive group. Have you talked to others who left?

Another way you can help others is to share your experience as a testimony. You need to be sufficiently recovered before you do this, so you can keep your emotions and words in control.

If you are attending a new church, you could arrange a meeting with the pastor to tell him the story of your difficult journey. If you have discerned that his ministry is grace-based, you can feel safe in doing this. You might want to ask a few questions to assure yourself that he will understand first. For instance, has he heard the term "spiritual abuse?" Has he ever witnessed it, or counseled someone who experienced it? Has he read any of the books on the subject? Ask him to define legalism. Offer him an example and see if he agrees, it is legalism. If he passes your examination, then you can feel some confidence that he will understand when you tell him your story. He needs to know about the dark side of misplaced faith. He might benefit in his teaching and counseling by knowing what spiritual abuse does to people. He may even call upon you to talk with another wounded believer at some point. When you can help another believer recover from spiritual abuse you will have come full circle.

QUESTIONS

1. Have you told your story to anyone yet? What was the response?

2. Have you talked to others who left an abusive group? What did you gain from the sharing?

3. Have you recovered sufficiently to tell your story as a testimony? What steps will you take to prepare?

TO STAY AND FIGHT

"Speaking the truth in times of universal deceit is a revolutionary act."

George Orwell

Many abuse victims have an intense desire to bring their abusers to account. If that is your intention you will need the support of wise advisors. You may also need to think outside the box for creative ways to accomplish your goal. There are ways this has been accomplished but there are real difficulties involved as well. It is a gutsy decision to stay in a high control group. Many heroes of the Christian faith attempted to bring reform to oppressive systems and found it to be a losing cause. You may want to keep in mind that it is worth a try but not worth your own spiritual health if you don't succeed.

Some groups that are legalistic or becoming judgmental may be quite sincere but misguided. In one instance the pastor of a church was becoming spiritually abusive, and people began to leave the church. Two ladies in the church read a book on spiritual abuse and immediately recognized the practices that were out of bounds. They approached the pastor with their concerns and gave him a copy of the book. He read it and was convicted. He began immediately to apologize to people, including those who left. People began to return to the church and revival broke out.

If you are going to stay and fight for your church, you must count the cost. You will become labeled as a troublemaker and will need to be able to disprove that label. You must conduct yourself with the utmost integrity. Any slight fault will justify the label they give you and your effort will cease to be of any effect.

At some point when you see that you cannot bring reform to the group, you may want to consider those individuals you can rescue. In one instance a member did not want to leave with her family still in the group. She called and asked for help. This was a very large cult-like group with many affiliate churches. She was successful in helping her family and friends out of the church and then the snowball began rolling. Today this so-called church has half its former membership and 90% of the affiliated churches have broken away. The Good Shepherd will come looking for His sheep, and sometimes you get to help.

QUESTIONS

1. Do you feel you have the fight and determination needed to stay and try to change the group? Explain.

2. Do you have family or friends in the group that you want to fight to free?

3. What help and allies have you assembled to assist you in your effort?

We love Him because He first loved us. We obey Him because we want to please Him (not to escape His wrath, because we are no longer subject to it.

My Personal Journal

"Be imitators of me, just as I also am of Christ"

1 Corinthians 11:1

9

Identifying True Christian Leadership

"We are not such fools as to refuse good bank notes because there are false ones in circulation."
William Booth

The foremost example of true spiritual leadership is Jesus. When people think of Jesus, words like *gentle* and *mild* come to mind. He was sought after during His ministry on earth by people with real needs; He cared for them, ministered to their needs, and left them with hope. Even people who knew they were sinners felt comfortable around Him. The people who thought themselves righteous, felt threatened.

Jesus provided the example to Christian leaders of the primary quality they should exemplify, that of a servant. The Pharisees, however, adopted a position-based authority because they placed themselves "in Moses' seat," the position of someone who would speak the words of God to man. They set themselves up as the authority on God. They did *not* follow up their positional authority with loving care for God's people. The story of the woman taken in adultery shows the Pharisees were more concerned for their rules than they were for people.

Jesus sought out people who knew they were sinners, who knew they needed help. He was not image-conscious, like the Pharisees and religious rulers. He did not think that His association with sinners soiled His own spirituality.

Even though He taught and exemplified servant leadership for three years with His disciples still they did not quite get it. When He saw them arguing about who would be greatest, He told them the greatest would be the one who served, not the one who sought to *be* served. Then He washed their feet, a humbling service reserved to lowly servants. With that act Jesus forever defined a Christian leader as one who is humble and seeks to equip believers with what they need to successfully live their life for Christ.

Jesus forever defined a Christian leader as one who is humble and seeks to equip believers with what they need to successfully live their life for Christ.

The Apostle Paul describes the qualifications of anyone who would serve as an elder in the church. This includes pastors.

> *"...if any man be above reproach, the husband of one wife, having children who believe, not accused of dissipation or rebellion. For the overseer must be above reproach as God's steward, not self-willed, not quick-tempered, not addicted to wine, not pugnacious, not fond of sordid gain, but hospitable, loving what is good, sensible, just, devout, self-controlled, holding fast the faithful word which is in accordance with the teaching, that he may be able both to exhort in sound doctrine and to refute those who contradict."*
>
> Titus 1:6-9

CHRISTIAN VIRTUES

These virtues should be evident in any Christian, but especially in leaders who are submitted to God's Spirit. They exemplify how Christian's should act toward one another. In Galatians Paul calls these virtues the fruit of the Spirit, in Galatians 5:22

> *"But the fruit of the Spirit is love, joy, peace, patience, kindness, goodness, faithfulness, gentleness, self-control; against such things there is no law."*

Jesus supports this at John 13:35,

> *"By this all men will know that you are My disciples, if you have love for one another."*

The Apostle John said at 1 John 4:8,

> *"...God is love."*

The fruit of the Spirit is love. Period. And love produces joy, peace, patience kindness, goodness, faithfulness, gentleness, and self-control.

Perhaps the most frequently repeated call in the New Testament is to love. We are to love God and our fellow man. All other virtues seem to flow from this such as the virtues listed above as the fruit of the Spirit. Perhaps Galatians 5:22 could be paraphrased and amplified as, "But the fruit of the Spirit is love. Period. And love produces joy, peace, patience, etc."

In high control groups this fruit of the Spirit is obviously missing. Especially absent is love. Consider the list of the fruit of the Spirit below contrasted with the fruit of an unholy spirit.

- **Love**—selflessly desiring the best for the one loved.
  Its absence is marked by selfishness, or worse, hate.

- **Joy**—a cheerful delight.
  Its absence includes gloom and sorrow.

- **Peace**—at one with God and others.
  Its absence is marked by strife and all that goes with it.

- **Patience**—forbearance and longsuffering.
  Its absence is impatience.

- **Kindness**—gentleness, goodness, graciousness toward others.
  Its absence brings unkindness, roughness and meanness, a lack of grace.

- **Goodness**—virtue, benevolence.
  The absence includes corruption and vices, lack of generosity.

- **Faithfulness**—Trust in God.
  The absence is marked by trust in self or in a man-made system. Unfaithful to God.

  Gentleness—a strength of conviction and character that is submissive to God, with meekness and tolerance. The absence is marked by intolerance and self-assertiveness.

- **Self-control**—temperance in all human passions.
  The absence is marked by yielding to human desires.

Paul sums up the conflict in human nature to which some surrender and others resist. He said,

> *"For you were called to freedom, brethren; only do not turn your freedom into an opportunity for the flesh, but through love serve one another. For the whole Law is fulfilled in one word, in the statement, 'You shall love your neighbor as yourself.' But if you bite and devour one another, take care lest you be consumed by one another."*
>
> Galatians 5:13-15

AUTHORITY AND SUBMISSION

Christian leaders do not have command authority over believers. They are not authorized by scripture to give orders or coerce submission. In fact, Jesus directly forbade Christian leaders commanding their followers.

Jesus said,

> *"But do not be called Rabbi; for one is your teacher, and you are all brothers. And do not call anyone on earth your father; for one is your Father, He who is in heaven. And do not be called leaders; for One is your Leader, that is Christ. But the greatest*

among you shall be your servant. And whoever shall exalt himself shall be humbled; and whoever humbles himself shall be exalted."

Matthew 23:8-12.

There is a place for a command authority structure such as the military, business, and government. In such settings it is an appropriate method of leadership and accountability.

A family or church should never be based on a command authority. Some teach what is called "the chain of command" as being appropriate for the church and family. The operative word in this teaching is *command*. The focus is on the task, not on the individual. Families and churches, however, are based on relationships and the focus should be on the individual. The "task" of the family and the church is to promote the personal growth of each member toward the fulfillment of that person's God-ordained purpose.

The only Christian authority in the Bible that is empowered to use coercion is the congregation of believers acting corporately to discipline a member. It has the power to require submission to scriptural standards. This is the final step in the process outlined in Matthew 18: 15-18.

> *"And if your brother sins, go and reprove him in private; if he listens to you, you have won your brother. But if he does not listen to you, take one or two more with you, so that by the mouth of two or three witnesses every fact may be confirmed. And if he refuses to listen to them, tell it to the whole church; and if he refuses to listen even to the church, let him be to you as a Gentile and a tax-gatherer. Truly I say to you, whatever you shall bind on earth shall be bound in heaven; and whatever you loose on earth shall be loosed in heaven."*

It is never the spiritual leader's role to exert such power. One verse that false spiritual leaders will misuse in this regard is Hebrews 13:17 which says,

> *"Obey your leaders and submit to them—for they keep watch over your souls, as those who will give an account—so that they may do this with joy, and not with groaning; for this would be unhelpful for you."*

To understand this passage, as with any verse, you must first ask to whom is it written? It is addressed to you, the believer. It is your verse, not his. It is your decision to obey, or not. But on what basis do you decide? You submit based upon your evaluation of the leader's own submission to biblical standards of doctrine, morality, ethics, and motives. The Apostle Paul illustrated it this way in 1 Corinthians 11:1: *"Be imitators of me, just as I also am of Christ."* It is clearly implied that if Paul did not imitate Christ's example, then those who had followed Paul should not continue to follow him.

> *Every Christian must discern as best he is able whether anything he trusts or gives credibility is worthy of that trust.*

Every Christian must discern as best he is able whether anything he trusts or gives credibility is worthy of that trust. Accountability in the New Testament church is a two-way street. If you are not able to sincerely ask questions, or respectfully point out problems, then you are in an unhealthy environment.

Hebrews 13:17 is not the only teaching in the New Testament on what our response as followers should be toward spiritual leaders. Paul commended the Bereans in Acts 17:11 for valuing the scripture more highly than his words. Thus, Paul endorsed being held to account for his use of scripture. A good Christian leader will not be offended by such scrutiny. Some may feel uneasy for lots of reasons, but they should never try to shut down your legitimate questioning.

An important doctrine that was revived in the Protestant Reformation was that of the "priesthood of the believer." This doctrine holds that every believer is individually authorized to enter the presence of God with his petitions. This doctrine began with the tearing of the temple veil at Christ's death, signifying that those whose sins were covered by the blood of Christ could now enter God's presence freely.

As God's children we are a brother or sister, a spiritual sibling, equal to every other believer. There are no priests with divine authority to act on behalf of a lesser class of believers. Brothers and sisters are equals. Spiritual leaders and laymen are equals before God. The leader does have a greater responsibility because of his teaching role, but that does not authorize him to command the sheep. His deepest desire is to please God and bless man, not to please and bless himself.

QUESTIONS...

1. What statements in this chapter registered most in your mind? Why?

2. What do you now understand to be the proper role of a spiritual leader? How is that different from your past understanding?

3. What was Paul's point regarding the Bereans?

My Personal Journal

"Be merciful, just as your Father is merciful."

Luke 6:36

10

Conclusion

Recovery from spiritual burnout after years of exertion on a legalistic treadmill or trying to put a life back together after experiencing spiritual abuse, is not a task for the faint of heart. It is real work. It takes the patience of Job and some of the wisdom of Solomon. But at the recovery end of the experience, you will find a spiritual maturity that is greater than at any time in your life. You will have matured through a difficult trial and will be stronger for it.

Your experience will have taught you that the world we live in is fallen. The people we rub shoulders with are sinners. Our own nature is also sinful. Given these conditions why should we have been surprised that people were selfish, proud, deceptive, and abusive? It is true that Christians are to live better than that and that the Church is to be a place of refuge, comfort, and encouragement. But if every Christian also retains a sinful nature, then it is only logical that we should expect to be sinned against, even by our Christian brothers and sisters. Only when Christ returns will this be changed. Until then we must take responsibility for ourselves, submit to the Word of God and His Spirit and act toward our fellow man with integrity. We must learn to be strong and stand with courage against wrong. We must learn the Truth so that we are continually set free and equipped to be salt and light in the world.

Your recovery equips you to help others so expect God to use you. A good way to start is to write out your experience as a testimony. Do it first for yourself. Then if you find later that God can use it in some way you will have it ready. In our ministry to survivors of cults, spiritual abuse, and legalism we find that testimonies are of great value. If you entrust us with your testimony, we will edit it for anonymity and use it to encourage others who feel they are all alone in their struggle.

"It was for freedom that Christ set us free; therefore keep standing firm and do not be subject again to a yoke of slavery."
Galatians 5:1

"The grace of the Lord Jesus Christ be with your spirit."
Philippians 4:23

My Personal Journal

The good person out of the good treasure of his heart brings forth what is good; and the evil person out of the evil treasure brings forth what is evil; for his mouth speaks from that which fills his heart.

Luke 6:45

APPENDIX A
Personal Stories

INTRODUCTION TO PERSONAL STORIES:

Ezekiel 34:1-10 describes the "shepherds of Israel" who feed themselves rather than the flock, who do not heal those who are hurting, or seek to bring back those who were driven away but rather discard them. They rule with force and cruelty. Jesus was most forceful and vocal in His denunciation of the spiritual abuse He encountered. See Matthew 21:12-13 and chapter 23.

I can write articles about the characteristics of spiritual abuse and describe its methods. I can tell you of the horrible effects it wreaks on the soul of its victims. But I cannot tell you how to feel about it. Until you feel the emotional and spiritual struggle these people face and see the callous and self-serving attitudes of abusive leaders, it is all academic information. There are many still in the grips of their own struggle for spiritual freedom. Many are also going on blindly in the deception that their "Group" is a healthy church. Please pray for these lost sheep that the Good Shepherd will find them.

The names of the high control religious groups in the Appendices are changed to avoid the idea that this workbook is about a specific religious group. It is not. It is about the failings of individual spiritual leaders and the control systems they put in place. It is about the failure of respect for the image of God in every individual, the sovereignty every person has over his own soul, and the gracious gift of freedom that is our privilege in God.

> "If men were humbly sensible of their own failings, they would not be very forward or pleased in judging others, for the censure passed upon others would but rest upon themselves. There are the same kinds of corruption in one man's heart as in another's; and if those persons that are most busy in censuring others would look within, and seriously examine their own hearts and lives, they might generally see the same dispositions and behaviour in themselves...which they see and judge in others."
>
> Jonathan Edwards, Charity, page 215.

D'S STORY

I was born into a religious family, the son of a mother from the Caribbean Island of Trinidad who was raised as I was, and a father who was brought up in another tradition and converted to the faith of my mother when they married.

There was really nothing out of the ordinary about my religious development at home, except that looking back I could point out that I was definitely taught about the importance of "The Church" as opposed to the importance of Jesus Christ.

I eventually left the church in pursuit of another expression of Christianity. I was once again focusing on joining the right church rather than knowing Christ personally. After some time at my local church, I was introduced to a communal group in Arizona. I eventually became a disciple of the leader.

After an initial period of a month or so, I began to be indoctrinated with teachings I was told not to reveal to anyone outside of the monastery's inner circle. I was taught to believe in conspiracy theories (some of which were that man never landed on the moon, that America is made up of a shadow government that is run by Masons and Jews) and that the Protocols of Zion are an authentic document rather than a work of racist fiction.

I was told that unless you give up sexual relations with your spouse, you cannot be holy in this life, while at the same time being taught that I should ceaselessly struggle to achieve holiness in this life no matter what the cost.

I was taught to whip myself with electrical cord when I had sinful thoughts and that this was normal behavior that the faithful indulged in.

I was taught to be obedient to my spiritual father as if he were Jesus Christ and that without his prayers, I would not make it to heaven when I die. This was the justification used to get me to be obedient to the teachings I have related.

I was taught to believe that there is a "shadow government" that is supposedly in operation in the world that is made up of Masons, the Illuminati, and "the Jews". This "shadow government" was said to control all of the governments of the world. I was told that part of their plan to do population control was to vaccinate the masses with immunizations that were deadly. Many of us were told never to immunize our children, that we should only use holistic remedies for our illnesses unless the doctor could be trusted and avoid Jewish doctors whenever possible (because in the Protocols one of the plots to kill Gentiles was via Jewish doctors who killed Gentile babies and adults whenever possible).

The Elder who founded of the communal group teaches in his book that our leaders are hierarchically the final successors of the Apostles through the Holy Spirit. Having been taught this, there was a while where in my mind he had apostolic authority to teach that the demons will drag me to hell when I die because I won't be able to ascend without my spiritual father's prayers if I disobey him. The Elder's book also says that we should never tolerate anyone who speaks against an "elder" because such a person is an antichrist, and we should oppose them immediately. I didn't want to become an "antichrist".

I was told that television, except for nature shows and things like that, were evil and that the best thing to do was to get rid of my TV. I was told the same thing about literature and music. I was taught not to read any secular literature and was told that the Bible and the Elders of the Church were all I needed to read. They said all music except for classical music and church music was a product of the Fall and not to listen to anything but that. Not having a television and not being able to listen to the radio, my main source of cultural information became e-mail and the telephone, or spending time with someone from the commune.

We had to get a blessing from our spiritual father for everything, whether it was dressing differently, changing jobs, selling our car, etc. I had to get a blessing even regarding what I could drink during the day and how many meals I could eat. All of this is called "voluntary" obedience by the way, except that you'll go to hell if you're not obedient because obedience fulfills all of the commandments of Christ.

I was refused a blessing to sell my car even though it kept breaking down on me and was the only means of transportation for my wife and I to get to work. We missed time from work because of all the breakdowns, which meant we missed pay. This also caused us to nearly get fired and put us so far behind in bills that we lost all of our savings. We eventually had to quit that job since they were going to fire us. Even though we finally decided to get a new vehicle just before that, it was repossessed later on, due to our lack of ability to pay since we had lost our income.

The Elder and I would talk a lot about the end of the world. He would mention it often. He said all the members of the commune would be martyred by being hung from the telephone poles. He also told me one year that by the summertime a war in the Middle East would break out over a dispute about territory and there would be a great war that a certain country would win. (I was given copies of these prophecies to put on a website I used to run with the Elder's blessing). When the prophesied events didn't happen, I went to the top leader, and asked him why, and he said he told me that just to be cautious. He had seemed pretty serious at the time he told me, however. He also told me on one occasion that I would most likely be "martyred", which stayed with me for a long time. I really believed that I should prepare to die.

When my mother was homeless, I was refused a blessing to go and help her over and over again. I finally decided to just go. My wife spoke to the Elder about it, and he gave his blessing grudgingly.

My wife and I had to confess all of our sexual activity including what went on, where we touched, and so forth. We had to confess any secular music we listened to, any TV shows or movies we watched, and anywhere that we went that wasn't "approved". I was even told once that I should never laugh, so anytime I found something funny I had to confess that I had "laughed frivolously".

I was required to confess all of my thoughts, both good and bad. If I couldn't confess directly, it had to be over the phone, and if I couldn't confess by phone, I had to write everything down and mail it to my spiritual father. It's very humiliating sending your private thoughts through the mail, but with everything they teach about obedience the rationale was that it was a small price to pay for eternal life. In the case that my spiritual father was not available there were only certain "approved" people I could confess to.

It was a nightmare once we were in the inner circle of the commune. Our lives deteriorated rapidly, our health was affected, and we were slowly being isolated from family and friends. Eventually, I decided to get my family away from their influence. Having moved to Florida after 2 years of going to Arizona weekly, I was able to spend 5 more years under their influence but out of their immediate reach. I thought I would be able to leave quietly and not tell anyone that I was leaving. I thought I would just disappear and never go back.

It didn't work. Because of some families whose children had been influenced by the commune, I decided to speak out, even going on television in Arizona to talk on air about the commune teachings. The backlash was very intense. I was called a liar, my life was threatened, and even Elders who had never met me were calling me "demonic."

At the time, I didn't realize that the commune was a cult. I simply thought it was a Christian group that was not a healthy place to be. It was when leaving began to take a very heavy toll on my wife and I that I realized it might have been worse than I thought. I was having nightmares regularly, panic attacks, severe depression set in, I was having suicidal thoughts, trouble controlling my anger, and I started drifting toward atheism.

It wasn't until a parent who had lost their child to the commune convinced me that it was a cult that I started to see any progress. He gave me literature showing what a cult is, pointed me in the direction of leading authors, and from there I found *Combating Cult Mind Control* by Dr. Steven Hassan.

The process for recovery was long and hard. My wife and I endured setback after setback, lots of periods of suicidal thoughts, and constant battles with depression and wrestling with the idea of God.

Through the contacts listed by Dr. Steven Hassan, I eventually reached out to the Watchman Fellowship. I'm very glad I did. I needed to know Christ; not a church, not religion, not the "right path", but Jesus Christ, the Son of God.

The *Spiritual Abuse Recovery Workbook* allowed me to take what I had learned from Dr. Hassan's material and face God again. It restored my faith in Christ's message as good news, rather than a nightmare, and gave me the strength to help lift my family out of bondage to the cult once and for all. I feel like an empowered Christian again.

It's been a long, hard road out of the cult, a journey that took over 3 years and carried with it a lot of tears, self-doubt, and setbacks. I truly felt while I was going through it as if I were literally in hell. But the good news is Christ is greater than hell, so it wasn't a place my family and I had to stay. He brought us out safely and we've been able to grow stronger than we've ever been.

It's not an easy path, but recovery is possible, and God is definitely with those who travel on it, always protecting, always guiding, and always loving.

JENNIFER'S STORY

My name is Jennifer and the Lord set my mother and I free on October 7, 2007. My mother and I were in a cult for 10 years. This is my story...

My aunt was in a Christian bookstore looking for a card for her son when the owner of the store approached her and started talking to her. After speaking to her for a few minutes he said that he had a word for her from the Lord. My aunt had been seeking the Lord's face for several years asking Him to send her to someone who really knew Him because she was not seeing the Lord in the churches she had attended. At this point in her life her son was going on a missions trip and her husband was quite ill. So, she thought, "could this be the person I had been praying for?"

She wasn't quite convinced but continued to go to the bookstore and then started "Deliverance Counseling" with him and his wife after hours at the bookstore. At first, she was skeptical but later felt that this was of the Lord and had seen some changes in her life. She told my mother and sister about this counseling because they too had really started to search for the Lord. My mother and sister also started going again being skeptical at first but then convinced this was of the Lord. They shared with me and suggested I go but I was married at the time and was fearful of anything "Spirit" filled because I did not understand the gifts of the Spirit.

In January '98 this man and woman were sending my sister out to California to marry a man she had never met, and they were to be the west coast side of their ministry. I went to say goodbye to her not knowing at the time she was going to get married and that is when I met them. They were different—especially him. He seemed to know so much about God and His word and then he had a word of knowledge for me. He asked me if I would pray a prayer with him to tear down my idols of having a child. He said that anything could be an idol and since I wanted it so badly, I was putting it before God. I said yes of course because I really wanted to serve the Lord. After praying he then gave me another word about my husband and how he would serve the Lord—at the time my husband was not saved so I was really excited.

So began my involvement with this "ministry". Deliverance ministries deal a lot with generational sin and curses as well as deliverance of demons. This was all new to me and although I was skeptical, I felt different like I was able to hear the Father's voice more clearly.

My husband was very upset about my involvement with this "ministry" and wanted me to stop seeing them for counseling, but I did not because I felt that he was asking me to choose between God and him and of course I was going to choose God. After several months he left me and later filed for divorce.

At this point the leader of this cult told me to quit my job, sell everything I owned, put my house up for sale and leave everyone behind. I was to ex-communicate myself from everyone who was not involved in the cult. He used scripture to back up everything he told me to do—such as "let the dead bury their dead" and "anyone who loves father or mother more than Me is not worthy of me" etc. ...

So, I sold everything I had, clothes and all, put my house up for sale, moved to another town and quit my job.

I didn't work for one year—they supported me for the most part however I did a lot of cash advances on credit cards for them. During that year I was with them every day I helped them around the house and ran errands with them. We watched a lot of movies because that is how he got his revelation on how the spirit realm worked and names of demons. He said that Satan revealed things about his kingdom through movies. Sometimes we would stay up all night watching all kinds of movies from drama, horror and even some x rated movies.

After about 6 months he hit me for the first time and then hugged me and told me that he was displaying the love of God that although He gets angry with us, He still loves us. I had seen him in rages before, but this was the first time he hit me.

All this time I was not able to see my aunt and my mother (who was living with my aunt) whenever I wanted—my mother couldn't even know where I lived. I was not to call her mother anymore because he had said that the Lord had given them to me as my parents, so I was to call them father and mother.

I know as you are reading this you might think how could I have not seen the red flags but all I can tell you was that it was so subtle so gradual and he used the Word to back up everything he did and because I was a baby in the Word I could not discern the half truths. Not to mention the fact that he told us if we left, we would go to hell.

Jumping ahead a few years my mother and I eventually moved in together because they said we had to—they picked the house and our furniture. He decided even what we wore. Shortly after this point my aunt left the cult and we were to have no contact with her because we would go to hell if we did. We had to throw out everything she gave us and never talk about her. About one year after that my sister and her husband also left the cult and again, we were not to ever contact her or even say her name.

About 4 years ago things started to get really bad—I was being beat every couple of months. He gave me black and blue eyes, broke my rib, broke my hand, threw me out of a car and left me on the side of the road till he came back for me. One beating he put a chair in the middle of the kitchen made me sit there while he beat me on the back with a slotted spoon. I had welts on my back for days.

He was taking more than half of our income. My mother and I were living in the same house but were not allowed to speak to each other or go anywhere. He had me working 72 hours a week and my mother was working 60 hours a week as waitresses, so we had cash to give him.

Then he even started abusing me sexually. This is hard for me to talk about because the enemy wants me to feel stupid and ashamed, but I know that by this point I was so worn down and I was so afraid of going to hell that I would do anything not to mention that I just didn't care anymore. This went on for 1½ years. I became pregnant and he made me have an abortion. This is the day I died—there was absolutely nothing left of me anymore —especially not spiritually.

I never told anyone not even my mom. When he would rebuke me, I would threaten to tell my mom so one day he told me that he had told my mother and that she believed him that it was all my fault. But he also told me that if we ever spoke about it that I would go to hell. So, I suffered in silence thinking that even my own mother blamed me and had deserted me.

During the last year I was told almost daily how much God hated me and that I was going to go to hell lest I repent, and God hated me worse than Satan and would punish me worse than Satan. I was also told that if I left the group then whomever I came in contact with would go to hell because of me. He would have me up for hours on the phone at night while I was working 72 hours a week. There were days I wouldn't get any sleep at all. He had a key to our house so we lived in fear that any minute he would come over. It was not uncommon for them to show up in the middle of the night.

Finally, God broke through and put a book in my hands called Spiritual Warfare by Richard Ing. In this book it talked about deliverance ministries and how sometimes the person doing deliverance can become prideful because of the power. He had heard of ministries that controlled the people in their ministries with things such as telling them what kind of car they could drive, who they could marry, where they should live and some even used deliverance as a reason to have sex with someone they are ministering to. This was everything that had happened to us—everything and he was saying that this appalled God.

At this point my mother and I started fasting and praying and talking. We couldn't talk in our home because he would always find out, so we started taking drives after work and crying out to the Lord. During one of these times my mother told me she knew what happened to me and she did not agree—I was so happy—there was hope.

The Lord also put Ira and Grace in the restaurant that we worked at who had a prayer-counseling ministry. And after a series of events, I finally got up enough courage to call her and ask for help. I didn't tell her anything I just asked her to pray with me to find out if what we were involved in was truly of God because if it was, we would stay if not we would leave. She started praying and the only thing she could sense was extreme fear and control which is not of God—she told me she felt we should leave.

Later that week we tried to leave but he came to our house at 2 AM and convinced us to stay. But the next week when Ira & Grace were in the restaurant my mother asked them to continue to pray for us because she wasn't convinced that it was of God anymore. At that point Grace was able to tell her all the Holy Spirit had revealed to her that week about what was going on—she knew that he was taking a lot of our money, he was controlling us with fear and that he was abusing me. We never told anyone this at all so this was all we needed and that night Praise GOD we left the ministry.

What God did for us after that, makes me weep to think of how he showered His love on us—one of my counselors says they are kisses from heaven.

SINCE LEAVING THE CULT —GOD:

Gave us a new place to live—we had to move out right away so he couldn't find us—our new landlord after hearing our story didn't even make us pay a security deposit and let us move in 10 days before the end of the month without charging us—so I could be and feel safe for the first time in years.

- Gave me credit to buy a new car—I had horrible credit because most of the time I didn't have enough money to pay my bills because I had to give him so much a month.
- Gave us furniture—mostly from friends—because we had sold all of our furniture.
- Gave us an inheritance that my uncle had been holding for my mother because my aunt told him that one day we would get out and we would need that money.
- Gave us wonderful counselors who worked with us diligently to set us free. Confirmed His word over and over again, to us when we started going back to church.
- Restored my relationship with my father—who I hadn't spoken with in 10 years.
- Restored our relationship with our family especially my aunt and my sister.
- Gave me a new husband—that is a miracle in itself, and is a whole separate story.
- And so much more…

God is so good—I cannot express to you enough how grateful I am to Him for setting me free—I am a completely different person. I still weep a lot especially during worship because it is overwhelming to me to think that He loves me so much and would do all this just for me.

I am only now starting to be able to read the Word—I stick mainly to Psalms and just praise Him for who He is. It's not as bad now but it's hard for me when I come across a scripture he would use—it's hard—sometimes the old familiar fear comes back but God has given me Psalms 35 as my weapon which I pray out loud. He has also given me a wonderful Christian husband who prays over me and with me when I get overwhelmed with the fear that I cannot fight for myself.

I am currently involved in counseling with a wonderful Spirit filled Christian woman for the abortion which is also helping a lot.

There is so much more I would love to share with you. I only told you the physical part, but the spiritual part of the cult would take too long to write.

My prayer since I have been out is, Lord please don't let all of this horror be for nothing. May Your name be glorified through it. I want to share my story not because of the horrible things I went through but for all the wonderful ways God is restoring my life—He is truly restoring all that the locust has eaten.

PAUL'S STORY

The following account is true, and much of it is shocking! The most shocking truth is that the cold steel of extreme abuse and control is no longer to be found just within the extremist cults. As documented in the growing number of books on the subject, spiritual abuse is very real and has found a home in too many of our Evangelical churches. Like a destructive virus, spiritual abuse is destroying the once safe haven of spiritual care, which thoughtful Christians once expected in their local church family!

My attempt to warn the unwary resulted not in bringing the abusers to accountability, but merely in me being labeled as yet another "rebellious malcontent."

Sadly, the above describes my personal experience with my once beloved home church and pastors! Tragically, my experience is very similar to that of former members and staff who I interviewed in preparation for this article. This experience also describes that of a growing number of the spiritually abused or victims of "friendly fire" within the church. Most tragically, my experience is eerily similar to the experience of those who exit cults. From the threats that leaving will place me outside of the will of God; to the loss of friends; to the threats against my career and reputation, to the practice of shunning; and on to the character assassination; there is little difference between my experience and that of a former cultist.

Spiritual Abuse Knows No Boundaries

Considering my standing and reputation, with the church and denomination, it never dawned on me that my own pastor would suddenly turn against me. It certainly never dawned on me that so many would blindly follow him to further enable him as a spiritual abuser. As a Christian Apologist and professional cult deprogrammer, I would notice the marks of spiritual abuse very early in the process. It never dawned on me that my own pastor would aggressively attempt to program the deprogrammer. My story demonstrates that no one is immune from becoming a target of spiritual abuse. What I have preached to others was proven true in my own case. Our spiritual enemy, the Devil, is no respecter of persons. Satan is an equal opportunity deceiver!

Behaviorist Definition of The Term "Cult"

Considering my work as a Christian Apologist, one would not expect that I would hold membership at a church that would meet the definition of "cult" in terms of behavior, methodology, and sanctions against dissenters. Now that 20/20 hindsight has been applied to my own experience, I reluctantly admit that I joined a church, which according to behaviorist definition is in fact a controlling, authoritarian "cult."

While many will not be pleased with the use of this term, I am not writing to please the majority. I am writing this article in the interests of objective truth, that is truth, which is true regardless of whether or not, one believes it to be true, and truth which is true regardless of whether or not one is comfortable with the facts. I am also writing to warn the unwary.

From Home Missionary—To Target of Spiritual Abuse

My experience began at my home church where my immediate family had fellowshipped for years. I was a home missionary (Christian Apologist), ordained with the Church denomination, and my church was one of several which provided missions support for my work defending the Christian faith. My work was successful in bringing many to Jesus Christ out of various cults and Atheism. The work was greatly appreciated by my home church and affiliate denominational churches.

My relationship with the two pastors covered three categories. They were my pastors who I loved and looked to for spiritual leadership. They were my fellow ordained colleagues. I also believed that my pastors were my personal friends. My experience to come would prove that I was seriously mistaken about the friendship as well as the trust.

Opening the Door to Spiritual Abuse

The spiritual abuse started shortly after I opened the door and allowed the senior pastor to "help me" through what was supposed to be "marriage counseling." I was the one who requested his help, but in retrospect, I realize that allowing him personal input into my life was the worst mistake of my entire life. This mistake would destroy my marriage, and significantly damage my career and reputation. I had no idea that I had opened the door to an individual whose primary interest was to dominate and control the lives of others. He was not the person that I knew to that point on a casual basis. On the contrary, he was an angry authoritarian with an inflated ego on a misguided mission to control and dominate anyone who opened the door to his influence. I had no idea that he was willing to destroy my marriage, career, and reputation if things were not done exactly his way.

At the pastor's request, my wife and I began meeting with him every Tuesday evening for "marriage counseling." Also at his insistence, I agreed to meet with him every Wednesday morning for what he called "accountability" purposes.

In both meetings he asked many rather personal, inappropriate, and intrusive questions. His questions about our sex life seemed strange and inappropriate, but we shared the information as requested. Since I was new to marriage counseling, I initially thought that his questions had a legitimate purpose. In the supposed "accountability" meetings, he asked many intrusive questions about the board members of the ministry where I am director; he talked down my board members and proceeded rather quickly to suggest personal friends of his who "would make better board members." Both his questions and suggestions made me suspicious of his intentions. I got the impression that he wanted me to dismiss the present board members and replace them with puppet board members of his choice! His quest for control soon became apparent.

I tried to explain to the pastor that my board had authority over me and that I did not have authority over them. I certainly did not have the authority to drop them and replace them with others as he was suggesting. I emphasized the fact that my board members had my utmost respect and trust, and that replacing them was out of the question. I also explained how uncomfortable I was with the pastor talking down my board members. He did not know any of them and therefore he had no basis on which to talk them down as he was doing.

For the first time, I began to notice, that my pastor was an angry person. He became angry when I did not agree with him, and he became angrily frustrated when I asked questions. I got a clear impression that he expected blind obedience to his suggestions. In this and several other meetings, the pastor's comments were repeatedly hyphenated with the phrase "I'm your pastor!" . . . "I'm your pastor."

At this point I began to distrust my pastor and I became understandably suspicious of his motives. I realized that, until this point, I really did not know him for who he really was. What happened next was cause for me to immediately call a halt to any more meetings with him, including the supposed marriage counseling and accountability meetings.

Heavy Duty Pastor Breaches Confidentiality; Has a Problem with Gossip

Over the following weekend I received two distressful telephone calls from fellow church members. Both shared a similar report concerning what happened when they were working at the church that week. It was brought to my attention that the senior pastor was openly gossiping with other church members at the church office. The subject was my wife and I, our marriage problems, and inappropriate details of our sex life!

Upon hearing these two reports, I immediately contacted the pastor by phone and explained that the weekly meetings were finished! Understandably upset and offended, I scolded the pastor for breaching my confidence and for openly gossiping about my wife and me. The pastor had been entrusted with confidential information, but he had blatantly betrayed our trust.

Interestingly, the pastor did not deny what he had done! Instead, he made overt threats about what would happen to me if I did not continue to meet with him for both the marriage counseling sessions and the supposed accountability meetings. His voice showed anger if not an uncontrollable temper. He promised to bring "severe consequences" to me if I did not continue both meetings. He also bragged about how powerful he was and how he could destroy my reputation and career!

I remember thinking, "Does anyone in the church know what kind of person they really have as pastor?" His behavior and comments showed me that I was just beginning to know the true person, and he was not at all the person he pretended to be on Sunday mornings!

He also said, "You don't have a choice" and his threats and assertions were hyphenated again by "I'm your Pastor." ... "I'm your Pastor." ... "I'm your Pastor." Once again, the way that the pastor used the phrase "I'm your Pastor" seemed to indicate that he expected blind obedience. I deduced from his anger, frustration, and overt threats that he was not accustomed to anyone standing up to him.

Decision to Leave My Home Church

In follow up to my telephone conversation, I also sent a letter to the pastor. I thought that this was necessary since he was not accepting my decision. I had also decided that I would need to look for another home church. My letter restated the fact that the meetings were finished and the reasons for my decision. Within a week, I received an inappropriate and extremely threatening letter, which was signed by both the senior and associate pastor. The letter explained that I "did not have a choice" and must continue to attend both meetings each week. The letter also threatened "consequences" if I did not immediately resume the meetings.

I responded to the letter in two ways, including sending another letter and arranging a meeting with the church board. My letter restated the issues, expressed disappointment that none of the issues were being addressed, and I expressed my displeasure that the pastors would use such authoritarian coercive tactics. My letter also expressed my opinion that, to my surprise, the pastors were behaving like cult leaders! I emphasized the fact that, as a Christian Apologist, I could not speak out against the controlling characteristics of cults while at the same time allowing my own pastors to use exactly the same, controlling behavior!

My request to meet with the church board failed. Only two members of the church board showed up. The two board members who met with me refused to discuss the pastor's offensive behavior or other pertinent issues. Since they refused to have any meaningful dialog, I wondered why they had bothered to show up for our meeting. The last time I had attended a similarly evasive meeting was when I tried to dialog with members of a secretive cult. It was apparent to me that the spiritual abuse was not limited to the senior pastor but was an integral part of church leadership collectively.

Unbalanced Church System

For many years the church system was unbalanced and biased in favor of the senior pastor. At business meetings no nominations for church board were accepted from the floor. Each year the pastor designated two persons who made up the "nominating committee." The pastor essentially told them who to nominate for the church board. Consequently, board members were always handpicked by the pastor and most often they were individuals who followed the pastor blindly. Although church members were allowed to vote, the ballet always said, "vote for eight" and there were exactly eight members to vote for. Since members could only vote Yes or No, his handpicked "nominees" were always voted in.

Threats, Slander, Coercion, And Financial Improprieties

Soon after I met with the two church board members, I received yet another threatening letter from the pastor. The letter was counter signed by the associate pastor and the board chairman. It was apparent that, even at this stage, the pastor had not given up on forcing me to resume the so-called marriage counseling and accountability meetings. His letter reaffirmed his assertion: "You don't have a choice."

Most telling, the pastor advised me that he was suspending payment of all further mission funds in support of my ministry until such time as I agreed to resume meetings with him! Interestingly, the funds, which he suspended, were already approved for the year by church membership. Consequently, this heavy-duty pastor suspended funds, which he had no ethical or legal right to touch. By doing so he inadvertently proved his abuse of power. He inadvertently demonstrated his willingness to use financial improprieties in his quest for ecclesiastical tyranny! Although I had done nothing to deserve his venom, his letter also attacked my character! In his letter he said, "You are a gifted public speaker, but good character is also important." Since I had done nothing to deserve such comments, reading his letter was very distressing and grieving!

To this point, the abusive pastor had discharged a volley of the weapons in his arsenal, including anger, intimidation, coercion, personal attacks, financial blackmail, and threats to destroy my career and reputation. Neither scripture nor professional ethics had stood in his way. Since he could not get his way, he opted for revenge instead. His next move: destroying a twenty-seven-year long marriage!

In the midst of the volley of weapons and venom, that my pastor had released at me, it was difficult for me to concentrate on much of anything. He was making my life unbearable, and I was still wondering what I had done to deserve such treatment! At this point I had to reevaluate the situation. I was being treated like I was guilty of some kind of serious sin, and yet the only thing I had done was to break off meetings with a pastor who breached my confidence by openly gossiping about my marriage. I had not fallen into sin or doctrinal error; there was no moral failure or financial improprieties on my part; and I had been true to my wife during what would have been twenty-eight years on our next anniversary.

I kept thinking: "What is he saying that I did?" "What is he telling his board and denominational officials"? I concluded that whatever he was saying were lies, and I was still trying to accept the unpleasant fact that my pastor was in fact a liar. Although I tried many times to find out what my supposed sin was, no one would tell me anything. The only information I ever received was reported to me by another church dissident from one of the denominational churches, which dropped financial support for my work. The reason was in fact a lie. I was dropped because my pastor said that I had some "spiritual discipline problems and was refusing to be accountable." Sadly, the language in this supposed reason was such that it left the "discipline problems" up to anyone's subjective imagination to determine what the issues were. I doubt if anyone would believe that the "spiritual discipline problems" were as simple as the real facts. I was being supposedly disciplined for refusing to allow an abusive pastor to continue counseling me; for trying to correct his error, and for attempting to bring the matter to the attention of the church board.

What about his comment that I supposedly lacked good character? What had I done to deserve such venom and slander? The answer was simple. From his perspective, I had dared to stand up to a man who thought that he was acting in the place of God. I had dared to "touch the Lord's anointed." (Ps.105:15)

No Denominational Accountability for Heavy Duty Pastor!
Pastor Destroys Twenty-Seven Year Marriage!

In desperation I contacted the denominational district office and I talked to the District Superintendent. He prayed with me on the phone and then asked me not to judge the entire denomination by the behavior of one pastor. If I understood him correctly, he was concerned about the pastor's behavior and agreed with me that the pastor was in error. Unfortunately, he would not agree with me that the pastor should be removed. The District Superintendent explained that I would need to send him a complete report in writing if I wanted him to look into the matter further. I sent him a seven-page report, which included all details. I underscored the fact that the abusive pastor was well into the process of destroying a twenty-seven-year marriage. I also sent the report to each church board member. I have now been waiting over two years, but nothing was ever done to bring the abusive pastor to accountability!

"He Who Pays the Piper Calls the Tune"

Unfortunately, this was exactly as predicted by a close friend who is a retired pastor with the same denomination. As he explained to me, the District Superintendent's salary is paid through contributions from denominational churches. Each pastor essentially controls how much is given toward the District Superintendent's salary. Since the District Superintendent is paid in part from the church in point, and the abusive pastor has complete control, the superintendent would not "bite the hand that feeds him." Tragically, the following phrase is descriptive: "He Who Pays the Piper Calls the Tune"

As explained later in this article, I genuinely believe that, according to behaviorist criteria, the church that I left is in fact a "cult." I do not believe that the denomination in point is in fact a "cult" collectively, because the denomination itself does not uniformly practice the same authoritarian control and sanctions against dissenters. Conversely, I believe that the denomination at the district level deserves severe criticism for failure to remove, censure, or bring any accountability to the abusive pastor and to church leaders who blindly followed him! In my opinion, the district superintendent ignored my report and clearly compromised spiritual truth for monetary gain.

Deceptive Appearance of Accountability

From the outside looking in, the structure of a denominational district and district superintendents gives the impression that pastors within the denomination have some form of accountability and a structure for correction when appropriate. In contrast, my experience demonstrates that with few exceptions, pastors within the denomination in point have no accountability whatsoever! As long as their church pays the district superintendent's salary, he will apparently look the other way. The denominational district in point lacks an objective structure to bring erring pastors accountability or correction when needed. The only exceptions that I know of are when erring pastors have limited influence, or when their actions cross over into legal areas such as arrest. Based on my investigation, I believe that this problem is limited to one district within the denomination in point.

I am aware of two cases locally in which a senior pastor and an associate pastor (from the same denomination but two separate churches) were both arrested for child molestation. In those cases, the denomination brought accountability and removed the pastors promptly. What is very sad is that in both cases, church members attempted to bring the matter to the attention of respective church boards, but the whistle blowers were told to be quiet and scolded instead! In both cases, the church boards and the denominational district took no action until after the law was involved! Members of the denomination in point need to be advised of this problem and appropriate actions need to be taken to correct this impropriety.

Abusive Pastor Turns My Wife Against Me

In the midst of the problems, created by the abusive pastor and the related lack of accountability, I was finding it difficult to concentrate on my work or family responsibilities from day to day. My life was becoming unbearable, and yet the worst was yet to come. In retaliation for me standing up to him, the pastor was busy turning my wife against me!

He convinced her to join with him in a strategy of contacting supportive churches and convincing them to drop missions support for my ministry. God only knows how he did it, but he actually convinced my wife that destroying her husband's career and reputation would be good for our marriage! This fact was explained to me by my wife, along with her assertion that, by not obeying the pastor I was "in rebellion against God."

Since we had both agreed to marriage counseling, there was a good chance at saving our marriage. The problems of our marriage had been present for the last fifteen years, but we had stayed together, nonetheless. Without the pastor's intervention and turning my wife against me, our marriage would not have ended. I had agreed to go to another counselor of our choice, but she would only agree to be counseled by the abusive pastor. The pastor had been very rigid in insisting that he was the only person who could counsel us and that we were not allowed to meet with any other counselor. In a very short time, I had watched helplessly as the abusive pastor literally programmed my wife to follow him blindly regardless of consequences.

Spiritual Abuse Strategy Includes Financial Blackmail

Very soon, all but one of the supporting denominational churches dropped their mission support of the ministry, which I represent. The remaining supportive church was in a different district. Just before each church notified me in writing, my wife would tell me which church would drop mission support next. She would tell me and then laugh about it! Very soon I had lost over one thousand dollars per month in missions support, which was designated to pay my salary. Very soon I did not have the money to pay bills or to buy groceries. When this happened, my wife gloated about it. She also goaded me with the promise that all of the lost missions support would be restored if I would resume the meetings with the pastor.

My wife also refused to buy any groceries or to pay any of the bills, which I normally paid. While I was starving, she was going out to lunch and dinner with friends. With no groceries, I began to starve. With no money to pay bills, the phone was soon disconnected, and the gas and electric service was scheduled for disconnection.

It was at this point that I sought professional counseling. I brought my problems to a colleague pastor who was a member of my ministry board. I also sought the assistance of several Christian counselors who specialized in spiritual abuse. The pastor friend referred to my wife's behavior as "reckless abandonment." He said, "Although she has not asked you to leave, by destroying your career and income and not paying any bills or providing groceries, she is forcing you to leave." He suggested that I needed a crisis intervention strategy to get my wife's attention. If I wanted to save my marriage, I would have to convince my wife to realize what she was doing by blindly following the abusive pastor.

Collectively, my counselors convinced me to separate from my wife and give her some time to realize what she was doing. Although I did not like the idea of a separation, I really did not have a choice. My wife had already told me that she would not pay any of the bills and that if the utilities were disconnected; she was planning to leave me. Consequently, I separated the day before the utilities were scheduled for disconnection and I moved in with a nephew.

Sadly, any hopes that this was to get my wife's attention were soon dashed. After my departure, my wife paid the past due utility bill and changed the locks on our home! She also resumed badgering me to "repent" and "come back to the pastor." She made it clear that I would not be welcome back until I accepted and honored the pastor again. In response, I explained that if I obeyed the pastor, I would be reinforcing serious sin and giving strength to ecclesiastical tyranny. I affirmed that, even if the pastor took away everything that I had, under no circumstances would I ever give honor or obedience to him again!

At this point I was broken; emotionally, spiritually, financially, and even physically! I was also very sleep deprived. Since I had not bowed to the abusive pastor, I had now lost my home, my career, and even my wife of twenty-seven years! What I wanted more than anything else was to have my wife and family back together again! The thought that divorce was the next step literally tore me apart inside. I loved my wife dearly, but I loved my Savior more! (Mt.19:29) My wife had also become a different person, programmed, and with a complete personality change. Nevertheless, I still had hope that it wasn't too late, and recovery was still possible.

As much as I wanted her back regardless of the cost, I simply could not turn my back on what I had preached to others during the last eighteen years in full time ministry. I had preached and lectured on cults and abusive religious groups; I had warned fellow Christians about not giving support to spiritual abuse; and I had led people from various cults to Jesus Christ, only to see them disowned by family members who remained spiritually captive to spiritual deception.

Now it was my turn to live what I had preached! Do I do what is right even when I must pay a significant price? (Or) Do I give in to the same evil spiritual abuse that I have fought most of my life and testified in court against, so that a power corrupted pastor can release the ransom that he was holding? (2 Sam. 24:24)

I was reminded of what several former cultists had said to me over the years. "Everyone gives up something to follow Jesus Christ. When someone comes out of a cult, they often give up loved ones." They were saying this because of the shunning practices of the cult from which they withdrew. Tragically, my experience with an abusive pastor in a mainstream church was very much like that of a cult.

In the final stages I could see that I was losing my wife and I therefore I begged the pastor (by phone and letter) to "cease and desist." When I explained that our marriage was going to end if he continued to take control of her, he did not care! His quest for power and complete control was considerably more important to him than saving our marriage. After the pastor turned my wife against me, she began asking for a divorce. Apparently, the pastor had convinced her to force me into filing for divorce. She was determined to have me do the filing so that she could look better in the perspective of the church.

During the final stages, a family member sent the money so that I could secure an attorney for two purposes. My attorney sent a letter to the pastor and church board warning them of prospective legal action if they continued destroying my marriage and defaming my character. My attorney also started the process of filing for divorce on my behalf.

At this late stage, it was still my prayer that my wife would reach a crisis point in which she would think objectively. I was hoping that when she was served with the divorce filing, this could force her to break off allegiance to the pastor and ask for the marriage to be saved. About a month after the divorce filing, I received a short burst of hope, but it quickly faded. My wife called and tearfully wanted to know if there was still any hope of saving our marriage. I said, "Yes" but she quickly added her condition that she must continue her blind obedience to the pastor and that I would have to live with that condition.

After my heart sank, I expressed my disappointment and explained that our marriage could not work under those conditions. I remember asking: "How could we attempt to save our marriage while simultaneously allowing the same abusive pastor to continue his unrelenting quest to destroy our marriage?" Tragically, my wife chose the abusive pastor over saving our marriage. Any God honoring pastor would have recused himself and put the marriage first. But not this pastor! His ego was far too great for him to humble himself before God and step aside to save a marriage.

Pastor's Behavior Offends My Children Away from The Faith

My family included my wife and our teenage son and daughter; a Christian family, which was broken up by my former senior pastor, and those who blindly supported his authoritarian control over church members. Our children had been raised in our Christian home and we were still paying off their schooling at a private Christian school.

Little did I know that all of our efforts to ground our children in the Christian faith were soon to be undone by my senior pastor. His unchristian behavior was to serve as the stimulus to turn my son and daughter away from the Church. My son and daughter watched helplessly as their pastor destroyed their parents' marriage of twenty-seven years, broke up their family, and attempted to destroy their dad's career and ministry reputation.

Now neither my son nor daughter attends Church any longer. Citing the hypocritical example of their former pastor and those who blindly followed him; they ask unanswered questions: Why would God allow such a person to be a pastor? Why doesn't the denomination fire him? Why is there no accountability for his actions? Why would God allow such an evil pastor to destroy their parent's marriage and family? Why is their mom continuing to blindly follow the pastor? (and) Why would God allow an evil hypocritical pastor to destroy the career and ministry dreams of their dad?

In answer to their questions, I emphasize that "People have let us down, but God has never let us down." I have underscored the fact that God had no part in the behavior of our former pastors; that their behavior is an example of corrupt human nature (Isa. 64:6; Rom. 5:12), and that what they intended for evil, God will use for good (Gen. 50:20). I prayerfully hope that time and better examples of the Christian faith will serve to bring my son and daughter back to trust in Christ again.

There was a price to pay for standing up to this heavy-duty pastor. I was to pay the price and be an example for anyone else who thought about standing up to this special pastor! After my experience, he would be able to tell dissidents what happened to the last person who challenged his will and authority!

Since my experience I have been contacted by several members, dissidents, and former staff of the same church. Some were concerned and wanted to see how I was doing. Many shared their opinion that I was wronged, but they were afraid to speak openly on my behalf. Sadly, several indicated that they wanted to seek another church, but were afraid of the pastor's wrath. How sad it is that many will stay in an abusive church because they are afraid to leave. Like the presentation by Jeremiah Films entitled "Fear Is The Master" too many Christians of our day are afraid to take a stand and afraid to stand up against evil. Edmond Burke is famous for the slogan: "The only thing necessary for evil to triumph is for good people to do nothing!"

I encourage anyone who is experiencing spiritual abuse to take a stand. An abusive leader depends on the people who stay and who continue to support an abusive system financially. Sure, there is a cost to taking a stand, but the cost is much greater for not taking a stand against evil. What about the cost of offended Christians who turn away from the faith? What about the cost of broken marriages? (and) What about the cost of allowing the collective Church to do nothing when the controlling practices of cults make their way into the Church?

Recovery: Where I Am Today

It seems appropriate to end this article by bringing the readers an update. I am still recovering from an experience very much like the experience of one who exits a "cult." Consequently, I have a counselor and two excellent pastors who are helping me toward successful recovery. I am indebted to David Henke of Watchman Fellowship for his kind understanding and assistance at different stages of the spiritual abuse and recovery process. His workbook: *Spiritual Abuse Recovery Workbook*, has been exceptionally helpful.

I am also indebted to Dr. Ronald Enroth of Westmont College for taking time from his demanding schedule to talk to me by phone during the early stages of my experience. I am deeply indebted to Dr. Enroth for his research, materials, and his books on the subject. His books, *Churches That Abuse*, *Recovering From Churches That Abuse*, and his lecture entitled "*Churches on the Fringe*" were exceptionally helpful.

The journey that I have completed has been difficult, but purposeful. I sincerely believe that what my abusers meant for evil, God will use for good! (Gen. 50:19) I now have a much better understanding of what it is actually like, to exit from a behaviorist cult. I know the trauma, the grief, and the negative experience of being shunned, losing friends, and living through a time when I did not trust anyone. I now know from experience the recovery processes.

Over the past eighteen years I have worked as a Christian Apologist. God has blessed my work with many decisions for Jesus Christ. Formerly, I did exit counseling (counseling those who exited cults) from an academic perspective. Now I will be able to counsel from both an academic and experiential perspective.

The damage to my career done by my former pastor and those who blindly followed him is substantial. Consequently, I am basically starting all over, rebuilding my ministry career as if it started a few months ago. And yet God is already blessing me again, providing new decisions for Jesus Christ, new speaking events, and new outreaches defending the Christian Faith (Jude 3). God called me to the special ministry of defending the faith many years ago. According to scripture, God's call remains on my life and work (Rom. 11:29).

I am now a member of a church in another denomination, and I have two pastors who I love and trust. This is significant because during the recovery process, I went through a time when I did not trust pastors. My pastors now are not only good shepherds, but they have proven to be caring, understanding, and helpful in my continued recovery process, and my experience growing in Jesus Christ.

PRESTON'S STORY

I know nothing of the world outside of The Bible Study Group. My father is a bible college student at the campus in Massachusetts and I am just four years old. I walk about campus holding my mother's hand. After our stop at the bookstore perhaps I will get an ice cream at the snack bar. "Where do we sleep tonight?" I asked. It had become a commonplace question in my young life. A week here, a month there. I don't know the names of the places I'm staying. I forget the faces, too. I remember cinderblock walls, basements, and cobwebs. I wake up in the night to the sleeping faces of strangers and check earnestly around the room to find the faces of my siblings and parents. Comforted, I pull the unfamiliar smell of the bedding around me and fall asleep.

"Why are those people looking at us like that?" I clutch the paper bag and follow my mother out of the grocery store. "They say 'beaker', mom. What does that mean?" My question is unanswered, and I get the distinct impression that they must be bad people. I'm sitting on the floor in a church service. My neck aches but at least I'm not in the chair again! My legs dangle and they ache so! I choose my crayons carefully as I hear Pastor's yelling getting louder. I smile because the yelling seems to make my father get excited. I don't really listen, but I hear words like 'authority' and 'wickedness.' God must be angry to use words like that. On the way home my daddy parroted parts of the message back to me and rumples my hair. Suddenly, I remember something. "What are cockatrice eggs, daddy? Will I get them, too?"[10]

We eat our meals in the cafeteria. So many people. It's a very big room. I worry about finding my way back to my mom's table. I scour the crowd for familiar faces, but I haven't found them yet. People look at me and smile like they know me, but they don't. Some families have tables and kitchens and it's just them together, eating. No strangers. We are staying in another dorm now, but I have to sleep down the hall from my mom and dad. When I'm in my bed I listen to the sounds of strange voices in the hall, laughing, talking, singing.

"We are moving again," my mother tells me on our way home from church. "Ok," I say. I don't like this new place. It's a big house but lots of people live there. I don't like to be on the stairs alone. Two sets of stairs. Its dark up there. I hear the call for dinner, but I don't want to go on the stairs. I don't like the top floor. Sometimes he locks me up there. Sometimes I run for the door, and he laughs at me because he is stronger. He touches me and I don't like it. My parents tell me it's safe here. We all love Jesus. I know I am a naughty girl. I know I have a bad secret. I play outdoors a lot. The field is open, and I can see in all directions. I like to climb trees. Climbing trees is a boy's game. I wish I was a boy; I think to myself. Then I would be safe. Safe and strong. I wonder if Jesus is angry with me.

I am sitting in a Wednesday night service doing my best to take notes. I glance around youth group section and see various teens around me, scribbling in their notebooks. Someone is moving their lips and I can tell they are counting the ceiling tiles. I don't think I belong here. My eye catches a youth assistant two rows over. His eyes meet mine and he smiles a knowing smile. I know he has been placed there on purpose to make sure he observes what we are "up to." The "minions" I jokingly called them. The college students who followed us around, shaking their fingers and impressing themselves with their own spirituality.

I am a marked teen. I know someone who left the ministry. They tell me I am infected with an evil report. They say they can sense a change in the atmosphere when I enter the room. I learn in youth group that evil reports can scar your soul for life. I am drawing a picture of what serpent's eggs must look like

10 Cockatrice eggs are serpent's eggs, the work of the devil.

in my notebook. I know the conversations stop when I walk in. I know they watch me. They will stop me to and from the bathroom in the quiet hallway. Trying to get out of service? They laugh.

I am sitting at the farthest table. The inner table is awash with joking and laughing. The loud voices of the youth leaders boom. The inner circle teens crowd around. Do they notice I am here? If I walk by, I know they will say hello but that is where they will leave it. There are no extra seats at that table. I'm frustrated because I've really tried to "get it:" what spiritual living is all about. I hear all the time that God is love. God is a personal God. He must be because, look how David and Moses talked to Him. I talk to Him like that. I ask Him to show me Who He is.

I've been called in to a private meeting again. It seems like the only time they acknowledge me. I notice there isn't another female present. Where was I yesterday, they want to know. They'd heard I was somewhere I wasn't supposed to be. I know. I saw those people watching me. I knew I would be reported on. Yesterday wasn't a church function. It was on my own time. My so-called private life. They sigh at me and exchange disappointed glances. I had high hopes for you, he says. I thought you would be making better decisions.

I am on a payphone talking to a friend. "Why aren't you in the meeting?" demands a voice. I look up to see one of The Minions. She gets in my face and grabs me by my arm. She tells me security can back her up if she needs it. Again, at a gas station, a pastor sees me in a vehicle with my friends from my neighborhood. He pounds his fist against the window, opens my door and tries to drag me from the vehicle. The pastor's wife is calling him from their car.... "let her go... just let her go." They shake their heads in sadness as they drive by us.

I walk along the sidewalk, smiling at the little girls on their tricycles. They wave and call my name. I love babysitting. Someday I will make a good mom. I hear their mothers sharply calling their names. Get indoors! Hurry, honey! The women come out to carry their children from reach of my "influence." They don't even attempt to hide the fact that they are peeking from behind their curtains.

I'm sitting in a youth study. I know the answer to the question he's asking. My hand is up, waving. I know! Call on me! He doesn't glance my way. He asks someone within the inner circle. Anyone else? My hand is still raised. "We need someone who has real insight," he says, emphasizing 'real.' At last, he answers the question himself. My ears burn with understanding. I read my bible on my own, but they wouldn't believe me if I told them. I see it is all pomp and circumstance. It is all a fake. I pray to the Lord. Show me what is real. Show me truth. He does not answer me now. Does He even hear? Maybe if I act like them, He will hear me...

But as I will one day find out, He will answer me, soon. I don't realize freedom is just around the corner.

I was 16. At last, I had it. Irrefutable proof that these so-called leaders had wronged me. My parents hadn't wanted to hear it, but they couldn't argue with the Bible. All the mocking, the shunning. It had gone on forever. I questioned a lot of things about myself, but I knew preaching something and adhering to it were two entirely different species in my church circles. I dug up the courage and faced my father. Deep in my pockets were scripture verses to back me up in case I should falter. My passport out of disgrace. "He embarrassed me on purpose, Dad. In front of everyone." I laid out the offense. "It isn't biblical for a youth leader to do that, is it?" I pulled out the crumpled verses and waited expectantly for confirmation. For validation. Acceptance.

The words my father spoke began my long journey to freedom. To getting out. Red faced, my father faced me and said passionately, "I don't care. You honor the MAN. You cover it. Don't ever repeat it. EVER. You honor the man."

I was crushed as it became clear I was not going to be protected from this. And then it struck me. Jesus…. He made himself of no reputation for me. His Father had allowed it too. It was a simple persecution I could suffer and though I didn't know it at the time there WAS a reason for His allowing it. I knew at that moment that I was seeing more clearly than anyone in my family. It was our Lord that received the honor. It was no man.

The incident when I was 16 was the first time, I had independently sought scripture myself in order to find truth. It has been the plumb line for defining truth ever since. Slowly as I moved into adulthood my childhood thinking fell to this way and that as I learned how to exercise critical thinking and weighing of scripture for the first time. I have since grown in the Lord and the more I know, the more I realize I have to learn. I stumbled upon an Internet website that discussed our Bible Study Group some months back, watched and waited, scoured the posts, gleaning all I could. I had thought I was fully healed from my past but the tendrils of defective teaching reach far. The ugly head of condemnation has to continually be cropped back. The posts on the website, particularly those from Massachusetts days, helped me precisely define the personal interpretation of the scripture that I might still be carrying even to this day. It has helped me shed things I didn't know I still carried.

My heart breaks for my "generation," the second-generation ministry kids. This wickedly flawed way of thinking is all we knew and at every turn it is force fed to us as truth. Many of us do not recover. Many of us forget God is the giver of the gift of our free volition and we do not use it to pursue Him on the outside. We justify that decision because man failed us.

That is precisely it. MAN FAILED US. God did not.

I continue on in my imperfect walk with God, nonetheless. The ministry had its hooks in me long enough. If I allow myself to continue in my wounds post Study Group, then I am still submitting to its perverse control. If you are reading this and you are hurting, yes! You were wronged. Yes, you may not ever be validated by the ones who hurt you. But don't stop living the life He intended for you.

There goes My child, her gait is grace;
Those words no time can ere erase.
Those loving words He spoke to me
In that dark time I could not see.
My thoughts were wild, my actions free;
And through it all, He still loved me!
He said that His redeeming grace
Could lift me from that place of waste.
And how He'd never let me fall,
And how He'd see me through it all.
I can but give Him love returned,
And put to use what I have learned.
There is one thing I cannot see,
How can I match His love for me!

~ Penned when I was 16.

Many people stay because the alternative is a loss they can't bear to deal with. Loss of parents, children, family, and friends. They stay and turn a blind eye because everything they know is there in the Study Group.

My decision to leave was costly. I lost my parents for several years, at a most crucial time in my young adult life... my late teens/early twenties. But the cost would have been unbearable if I'd stayed.

I leave a wake of mistakes behind me, but my past wrongs do not eternally scar my soul as I was led to believe. God does not practice within the confines of the Bible Study Group box.

My mother once confronted youth leadership in Baltimore about the teens that were left to slip through the cracks. Leadership's reply was this: "I am not here for the ones that cause trouble." Come again?? Just exactly WHO determines whether a teen is deemed worthy of investment? How ... . is that determination made?

Wickedness. It belies the very title they claim possession of: Youth MINISTRY.

RESPONSE TO PRESTON'S LETTER

After Preston posted her story on the Internet many who are now out of the Group posted their responses to her. The following are a couple of them:

Dear Preston,

I am horrified and feel incredible guilt and sorrow. I am so so sorry. I am certain I was a part of your life, and I did not protect you. As a mother I feel sickened that we did not protect our children, did not protect you... I am horrified because I KNOW your story is not an isolated case. You are a gifted writer, and your story resonates to all of us. Please keep writing as you are helping many of the 2nd generationer's as you write. The names are not important, the names changed but the abuse was the same. The reflection of you walking the campus of Massachusetts and a teen in Maryland is so powerful. A friend called me in Massachusetts last night to share how your words affected her.

I love you Preston, please forgive me for not seeing the Group world through your eyes and not rushing to your defense. Please forgive me... JB.

◆ ◆ ◆

Dear Preston,

I, too, am sickened by your story, and as JB said so well, feel incredible guilt and sorrow. I was probably in your world, too ... I had a child who cried out to me many times, but I was blinded. Like Bob said, there were signs, so many signs that things were wrong. I did not protect my own child, or the many young people I had the privilege of knowing. Honor authority, submit, never speak negativity, obey ... I taught what I was taught. How can I express the depth of my regret? I am so deeply, deeply sorry.

My Personal Journal

"who comforts us in all our affliction so that we will be able to comfort those who are in any affliction with the comfort with which we ourselves are comforted by God."

2 Corinthians 1:4

APPENDIX B
Author's Experience and Insights

MEETINGS WITH THE SPIRITUALLY ABUSED

"Ye shall know the truth and the truth shall set you free."
John 8:32

In the mid-90's I wrote our Watchman Fellowship ***Profile*** on Spiritual Abuse and shortly thereafter people began to call asking for help.

It occurred to me when the first caller described a spiritually abusive leader that there must be others in their group who had the same experience. I began to ask other callers if they knew of "dissidents" like themselves. The frequent reply was a strong "Yes!" I then asked if the caller thought these dissidents would attend a meeting to learn about the dynamics of spiritually abusive systems as a way to learn what happened to them. Most said it would be welcomed. Since that time, I have met with, or advised, a number of such dissident groups to educate them on the abuse dynamics and put them on a path toward spiritual recovery.

THE FIRST CALL

The first call requesting help came from a couple involved in a group here in Georgia. Let's call them The XYZ Group. The wife described a spiritual leader who was a controlling type of personality who showed no mercy, forbearance, or grace. He would doggedly pursue any perceived lack of loyalty, questioning of leadership, or lack of attendance. He even pursued her husband to his job site to confront him about some perceived disobedience. This leader, in effect, was robbing the man's employer. Needless to say, his sense of boundaries was deficient.

This and other such examples of a controlling personality caused me to think there would be a lot of such people who experienced his control. When I asked about that the caller said, "Yes, there are lots of people who have left over such things." When I asked if she could get them together for a meeting, she said she would try and later called to say there would be a couple dozen people who would come to their home.

I then began to consider how to conduct this meeting. It occurred to me that because The XYZ Group in question was essentially orthodox in its doctrine I could create the impression that Watchman Fellowship, a ministry to cults, was now going after Christian groups that we didn't like. That perception, though totally wrong, could close doors to our wider ministry. So, the question I faced was how to deal with the abusive control of people without being perceived as "going after" an otherwise Christian group.

I also realized that the leader of The XYZ Group would probably come after me if he got wind of the meeting. Though I was not concerned on a personal level I had to think of the larger ministry and that potential for public misperception of our purpose and goal.

I decided I would not "deal with" The XYZ Group at all. I would focus entirely on the characteristics of a legalistic and abusive system. I would give those in attendance the opportunity to describe how each characteristic I described was manifested in The XYZ Group. In this way I could not, nor could Watchman Fellowship, be accused of "going after" a doctrinally orthodox group. My purpose would be entirely restricted to providing insight into how all abusive systems function regardless of doctrine, how spiritual abuse damages people, and how healing can be found.

THE DISSIDENT MEETING

There was an apprehension among some that the meeting would be infiltrated or spied upon by The XYZ Group. To forestall this all invitations were by word of mouth and only those invited were allowed in the door. No one came who was not invited which gave a sense of relief to those concerned.

To provide further assurance I asked all present to raise their hands if they agreed to keep all our discussions confidential. This is very important for people who are fearful of retribution that might be imposed on them or their family. All raised their hands.

SYMPTOMS OF THE SPIRITUAL ABUSED

It is extremely important when ministering to the spiritually abused to understand their mental and emotional condition. Here are a few of the most important symptoms:

1. Abusive systems train their members to be **paranoid and distrustful** of outsiders. If you are going to help these people you have to earn their trust with positive and affirming counsel.
2. Abuse victims frequently **doubt their own thinking**. Having been taught one "truth" that has not worked out as expected they are in a kind of spiritual limbo. They frequently don't know how to evaluate truth claims.
3. Members are frequently **depressed emotionally and spiritually**. They need to hear a message of hope from someone who will care about them.
4. Most feel that they are **all alone** and no one else shares their doubts and fears. In high control groups dissent, questioning, and doubting are treated as the worst kind of sin. People who do question are marked and punished. To avoid the punishment, people keep their doubts to themselves. This is why they feel alone. One of the most liberating feelings is to learn that they are not, in fact, alone.

5. Many are **very tired**. Legalistic groups will put people on spiritual performance treadmills that have the effect of draining away any passion and energy for service. They need to know that God wants them to get the rest and healing they need. He isn't calling them to more work when they are not able.
6. **Relationships are broken or threatened.** Because people cannot deal openly and honestly with problems, tension and stress develops; that impacts relationships. This is especially difficult when it involves family and close friends because the organization represents God and God is more important than family or friends.
7. Most **feel powerless** to change things for the better. Being powerless is learned in high control groups. They want you to depend on the leader or group. They want to control the things that affect the organization's image, resources, and unity. So, they condition their followers to look to them as God's authority, to over-commit their time and money, and never question. All this leads to a loss of will to think and act independently in one's own self-interest.

To start the meeting, I asked the homeowner to lead in prayer. Afterward I introduced myself as someone who had been dealing with high control groups for many years. I also said my purpose and goal for the evening was to help them by describing and defining legalism, spiritual abuse, and mind control. They would decide if anything I said fit their experience, or not. I was not going to say a word, positive or negative, about The XYZ Group. I was not there to approve or disapprove of anything.

I did not come with financial payment in mind. Since The XYZ Group is located in a nearby town it was a short drive from my home, so I did not need my expenses covered. Watchman Fellowship's financial policy when speaking in a church is to ask for travel expense plus a love offering. In the case of meeting with spiritual abuse dissidents I have said nothing about money. This policy is important because the abusive group will definitely try to label me as a "hired gun" and the abuse victims have heard too much about their money obligations already. In most cases donations were offered.

I spent the rest of the evening describing legalism, spiritual abuse, and mind control as a pyramid structure with three levels of a performance-based attempt to gain God's favor. The seedbed for abuse is the first level, legalism.

Legalism is defined in Matthew 15:9b as "teaching for doctrine the commandments of men." It is a usurpation of God's role as Lawgiver. It also leads to a usurpation of the Holy Spirit's role to convict of sin. Legalism will inevitably lead to rules becoming more important than the person. When that happens, spiritual abuse begins to take place. This leads to the second level, active control or injury of the follower, or spiritual abuse.

Spiritual abuse is the injury of another person's spiritual health. The cause can arise from a doctrinal error that puts a person into a performance-based relationship with God. Or, it could be the result of a spiritual leader trying to meet a legitimate need by an illegitimate means at the expense of another person's spiritual health. When leaders seek power, prestige, or the purse, for its own reward and the followers are used to further that goal then the third stage of mind control may be reached.

Mind control is extreme spiritual abuse. It is at this stage that people "drink the Kool-Aid." Many of the characteristics of spiritual abuse and mind control overlap. The difference is in the degree of severity. Dr.

Robert J. Lifton defined this psychological phenomenon in his book ***Thought Reform and the Psychology of Totalism.*** His book was an outgrowth of his study of American POW's released from communist prison camps after the Korean War.

As I began to describe legalism's characteristics, I suggested that people could raise their hand to offer an example from their experience that illustrated the characteristic. No one offered examples for the first few characteristics. Then one brave individual raised her hand and described how the characteristic I was explaining fit The XYZ Group. After that there were multiple hands raised for every characteristic, I explained.

I saw an interesting thing begin to happen as the evening wore on. The big word for it is "consensual validation." One's experience and opinion about it are validated when they see it is part of a larger consensus. People commented repeatedly that they thought they were the only one who noticed this or that. And there was a light in their eyes as they realized that their ordeal was now over, and they had hope for a healthy future. They were smiling, joking, agreeing with one another, sharing insights and experiences as a way of validating themselves. They had a name for what happened, spiritual abuse, and they were now free from it.

As I left that night to return home, I told my wife Carole, that the experience of that evening was the most fulfilling I had ever had in the ministry. To see God's people, turn from fear and dread to hope and excitement in one evening is exhilarating.

The leader of The XYZ Group got wind of the meeting afterward and began to pursue me for answers to his questions. He left numerous messages on my answering machine demanding that I turn over everything I had in my files about him and The XYZ Group. I had no files so that was easy. I also told him that if I did have a file, I would not share it with him. If he wanted to know what people had told me he could ask those who were at the meeting. But since I didn't record their names, I couldn't help him there either. His demanding and irate manner told me that he was not interested in solving the problem his people described. He was only interested in putting an end to dissent and warning this outsider to stay away.

A couple months later I spoke at a conference on cults in west Georgia. I wasn't surprised to see this leader in attendance. However, I was concerned that he might interrupt the conference with his own agenda. He waited until the conference was over and confronted me in the parking lot. Again, I told him there was no file. Nor was there any intent on my part to publish anything. My meeting with his former members was confidential and for their benefit only. I did suggest strongly that with so many of his former members in agreement about the same set of problems then maybe his real problem was within himself. He didn't like that comment but saw he wasn't able to intimidate me like he could his members, so he agreed to disagree, to put it nicely.

ANOTHER DISSIDENT MEETING

The next call came from a much smaller group in east Alabama. A couple of former members were attending a different church trying to restart their spiritual lives. They were also trying to help the pastor understand their experience. This was a new thing for the pastor, and he felt at a loss to understand the damage that had been done and how to help. I asked if he would host a meeting for any dissidents from that group who would be willing to meet. He gladly offered the church as a meeting place.

This group of dissidents was smaller than The XYZ dissidents. Their experiences were different too. However, they identified with the characteristics of legalism and spiritual abuse that applied to their group. Not all high control groups exhibit all the characteristics. You could say some specialize.

Having a pastor offer his church as a meeting place brings to mind that many times victims of legalism and spiritual abuse leave an unhealthy environment and go to another church without the benefit of a learning and healing process. Pastors should know there may be people in their church who need to resolve unhealthy spiritual experiences in their past. Watchman Fellowship can help.

SUBSEQUENT MEETINGS AND CALLS

There have been numerous calls and emails from people seeking help. They have come from groups in North Carolina, Maryland, New Jersey, Tennessee, Texas, and other States. Individuals have called or emailed from almost all the States. Because of the number I found that I needed a tool that I could use to help them understand what had happened and how to recover from it. I began to write a weekly Spiritual Abuse E-Letter that was posted online. After that I realized that I needed to put the content of those E-Letters into a more permanent format. That is when I came up with the idea for the ***Spiritual Abuse Recovery Workbook.***

The format is essentially the same as what I did when I met with the dissidents from The XYZ Group. I don't name groups. I deal only with the ideas and practices. This is important because to name any group is to communicate that what I am saying is only about that group and not the one the reader was in. The individuals need to make the connection for themselves that what I describe fits their experience, or it doesn't. I can't tell them it does. Nor can anyone else.

Evidently there is a growing phenomenon of poorly trained and improperly equipped spiritual leaders. There is also a growing number of heretical and fad teachings that lead to a performance-based relationship with God. When you combine these elements, the results are many people experiencing spiritual damage and confusion.

Many books have been written on the topic. That fact by itself demonstrates that there is a growing phenomenon in the church. It also demonstrates that a lot of people are in the same boat of confusion, false guilt, and a feeling of being alone in their struggle.

My Personal Journal

"for His divine power has granted to us everything pertaining to life and godliness, through the true knowledge of Him who called us by His own glory and excellence."

2 Peter 1:3

Additional Resources

RESOURCES COVERED ON FOLLOWING 6 PAGES:

CHARACTERISTICS OF A SPIRITUALLY ABUSIVE GROUP:

- ✓ Blame misfortune on lack of faith
- ✓ Label those who dissent
- ✓ Put you on a performance treadmill
- ✓ Claim a superior status with God
- ✓ Close you off from outsiders
- ✓ Provide no accountability for leaders
- ✓ Emphasize conformity to legalistic rules
- ✓ Label former members as unspiritual
- ✓ Use fear and guilt to manipulate you to comply
- ✓ Focus on the leader's positions of authority
- ✓ Wound people spiritually and emotionally
- ✓ Try to control your time and sources of information
- ✓ Shut off discussion about forbidden subjects

If you identify with any of the above characteristics you may have experienced spiritual abuse.

Recovery Scale

Every individual's recovery from spiritual abuse and deception is unique. Your journey back to spiritual, emotional and personal wholeness may take months or years—yet it will happen, if you work at it. Along the way, you'll wonder how you're doing. The scale below can give you a gauge of how far you've come, and encourage you that the remaining steps are possible. You may not complete all the steps, or in this order, but you CAN recover.

Where are you on the scale today?

____

____

____

BONDAGE

15	I am **involved in my group** and happy.
14	I am **beginning to feel discontent** with questions and confusion.
13	I have **serious thoughts about leaving** the group.
12	I am preparing to exit the group.
11	I have **broken** with the group.
10	**My new life has begun** (job, home, daily routine, spiritual quest).
9	I have **begun receiving community.**
8	I am **making new friends.**
7	I am **seriously and honestly evaluating** my experiences.
6	I have **found a supportive community.**
5	I am **trying new churches.**
4	I have **settled into a church.**
3	I have **processed my experiences** to the point of being **able to help** others.
2	I have **forgiven the abusers and myself.**
1	**Positive spiritual experiences** have become the norm.

FREEDOM

What steps can you take to move ahead?

____

____

____

THE GOSPEL SIMPLY STATED

"Now I make known to you, brethren, the gospel which I preached to you, which also you received, in which also you stand, by which also you are saved, if you hold fast the word which I preached to you, unless you believed in vain. For I delivered to you as of first importance what I also received, that Christ died for our sins according to the Scriptures, and that He was buried, and that He was raised on the third day according to the Scriptures, and that He appeared to Cephas, then to the twelve."

1 Corinthians 15:1-4

Man is alienated from a holy God because of sin:

"Therefore, just as through one man sin entered into the world, and death through sin, and so death spread to all men, because all sinned."

Romans 5:12

Man's deeds are insufficient toward his own salvation:

"For all of us have become like one who is unclean, and all our righteous deeds are like a filthy garment."

Isaiah 64:6

"For by grace you have been saved through faith; and that not of yourselves, it is the gift of God; not as a result of works, that no one should boast."

Ephesians 2:8-9

God, the Father, took the initiative to satisfy His holy requirement of justice by paying the price, in the Person of His Son, Jesus Christ:

"For God so loved the world, that He gave His only begotten Son, that whoever believes in Him should not perish, but have eternal life."

John 3:16

Man's only "work" is the act of faith, confessing our need of a Savior and placing our trust in His payment for the penalty of our sin:

"They said therefore to Him 'What shall we do, that we may work the works of God?' Jesus answered and said to them, 'This is the work of God, that you believe in Him who He has sent.'"

John 6:28-29

God then applies the payment, the blood of Jesus, to our account. That blood covers our sin and thereafter God only sees the righteous blood of His own Son:

> *"Much more then, having been justified by His blood, we shall be saved from the wrath of God through Him."*
>
> Romans 5:9

> "If we confess our sins, He is faithful and righteous to forgive us our sins and to cleanse of from all unrighteousness."
>
> 1 John 1:9

God then gives us the gift of His Holy Spirit, to indwell us. The Spirit then convicts us when we sin, comforts us, and guides us into all truth:

> *"But when He, the Spirit of truth, comes He will guide you into all the truth; for He will not speak on His own initiative, but whatever He hears, He will speak; and He will disclose to you what is to come."*
>
> John 16:13

The indwelling Holy Spirit is God's down payment on our final and complete redemption:

> *"Now He who establishes us with you in Christ and anointed us is God, who also sealed us and gave us the Spirit in our hearts as a pledge."*
>
> 2 Corinthians 1:22

RECOMMENDED READING

Non-Fiction

Healing Spiritual Abuse
by Ken Blue
Published by Intervarsity Press

The Subtle Power of Spiritual Abuse
by David Johnson and Jeff VanVonderen
Published by Bethany House Publishers

Tired of Trying to Measure Up
by Jeff VanVonderen
Published by Bethany House Publishers

Families Where Grace is in Place
by Jeff VanVonderen
Published by Bethany House Publishers

Toxic Faith
by Jack Felton and Stephen Arterburn
Published by Shaw

Recovering From Churches That Abuse
by Ronald M. Enroth
Published by Zondervan

Fiction

***Wisdom Hunter**
by Randall Arthur
Published by Multnomah

***Betrayal**
by Randall Arthur
Published by the W Publishing Group

***The Gathering Place**
by Becca Anderson
Published by River Oak

* These books are fiction. They take the reader through the emotional learning about unhealthy religious experiences while affirming the healing effect of God's grace. Highly recommended!

BOOKS LISTED BELOW ARE OUT OF PRINT

* However they are available "used" on Amazon

When God's People Let You Down
by Jeff VanVonderen
Published by Bethany House Publishers

Damaged Disciples
by Ron and Vicki Burks
Published by Zondervan

Breaking Free:
Rescuing Families from the Clutches of Legalism
by David R. Miller
Published by Baker Book House

Churches That Abuse
by Ronald M. Enroth
Published by Zondervan

My Personal Journal

"I have treasured Your word in my heart,
So that I may not sin against You."

Psalm 119:11

Acknowledgments

Several people have given their assistance in the writing of this workbook.

I want to thank Becca Anderson, author of *The Gathering Place*, who gave me many editing suggestions, practical insights into the arrangement of the original manuscript, and help with the graphics.

I also want to thank Judy Pope, a licensed counselor at the Pastoral Institute in Columbus, GA, for her helpful suggestions.

And thanks to my wonderful wife, Carole, for her patience with the layout, editing and endless hours of listening and practical help.

Need Help?

Are you someone that is trying to make sense of a spiritual abusive experience? If so, I would like to hear from you. Feel free to reach out to me. I believe we can help. Rest assured, if you need me to keep your identity confidential, I will honor that.

My contact information is below:

David Henke

Email: dhenkewatchman@gmail.com

Watchman Fellowship of Georgia
P.O. Box 7681
Columbus, GA 31908

Website: www.watchman-ga.org